Science in the Service of Mankind

THE BATTELLE STORY

Science in the Service of Mankind

by
George A. W. Boehm
Alex Groner

LEXINGTON BOOKS
D. C. Heath and Company
Lexington, Massachusetts
Toronto   London

O. K. Devin, Inc. / design
Michael Casad / illustrations

International Standard Book Number: 0-669-83584-6

Library of Congress Catalog Card Number: 72-148

Table of Contents

Foreword

My career as a researcher and research manager—nearly half of my life—has been spent at Battelle Memorial Institute. Both as a newcomer and later as I achieved the status of an "old hand," I was always intrigued with the fact that almost every Battelle staff member had his own version of the history of Battelle. The general framework was always the same, but the details varied slightly, depending on the teller. When I became President of Battelle, I determined that one of my early efforts would be directed toward the preparation of a formal written history of Battelle.

In reviewing the possible author candidates, it was obvious that many Battelle oldtimers would welcome the assignment. However, it was also obvious that the least subjective perspective on Battelle would be that of an outsider knowledgeable in the area of science and technology and familiar with the business scene. The author—in my view—also needed to be a senior person, so that the events of the early '30s would be more than childhood remembrances.

With this view, then, we commissioned the authors to come into Battelle and prepare a history of our organization from the same independent base that they would employ if they were on an editorial assignment for a major business magazine. My suggestions to the authors were simply that we wanted balance and perspective, which recognized that Battelle operated in the broad environment of the business world and not in the isolation of the ivory tower of science and technology.

We have taken few liberties with the authors' original manuscript. All of our suggestions have been considered by them—some accepted, some rejected. In the cases of selected details—a date, a contract amount, a specific title of a research project—where our detailed knowledge was superior, they naturally agreed.

My impression after reading the final draft is that the authors have done an excellent job in writing a very readable story that tells it like it was and is. Although I have an obvious bias, I hope you will find the Battelle story as interesting as I do.

S. L. Fawcett
President
Battelle Memorial Institute

December 30, 1971

Authors' Preface

For us this story begins in April of 1970, when Clyde R. Tipton, Jr., Coordinator, Corporate Communications for Battelle, phoned one of us (Boehm) from Columbus, Ohio. Mr. Tipton said that Battelle wanted a history and independent assessment of its position in and contribution to the American scene. It was not to celebrate any special event or anniversary, he explained, but something that ought to be done—now.

The opportunity to look deeply into Battelle's forty-odd years was rapidly vanishing. Despite its size and complexity, the Institute had never kept much of an archive; also, many of the people who knew Battelle at first hand from its earliest days were dying off or dispersing.

To a writer specializing in science and technology, the prospect was irresistible. The chance to study the Institute in depth was unique. Battelle is the biggest single operator in American industrial research, and yet to the press and public its accomplishments were little known and its operations were a mystery.

But one writer—Boehm—was just starting a major project: the U.S. Metric Study for the National Bureau of Standards. Besides, he wanted to work with someone well versed in the business aspects of an organization such as Battelle. Tipton agreed to a collaboration between Boehm and Groner, who was engaged in writing a history of American business for American Heritage.

We began our preliminary work in the fall of 1970. We examined documents and conducted some general interviews. Before long we had a list of fifty-four people we wanted to interview (we actually talked to ninety-seven). Some of the interviews were conducted in two or three sessions and lasted as long as eight hours; no interview took less than an hour. Travels took us to Richland, Washington; Santa Monica, California; Minneapolis, Minnesota; Kansas City, Missouri; Washington, D.C., and Cambridge, Massachusetts, among many other places.

We interviewed Battelle people passing through to and from Europe; alumni who had known Battelle from its early days; scientists, engineers, and executives who had done business with Battelle through the years; and members of the technical press, who should know Battelle if anyone does. Columbus, site of the original laboratory, was the hub of our wheel. There we interviewed thirty-six staff members whose tenures ranged from five to almost forty years. And there we also saw those who had known the man who founded the Institute, Gordon Battelle.

As we began to learn more and more about Battelle, its scope of operations, its size, its past accomplishments, and its promise, we became fascinated with the subject. How could the institution have contributed so much to the mainstream of scientific and technological development and yet remain virtually anonymous to most Americans?

In time, our research led us to some of the answers. For one thing, Battelle Memorial Institute was the lengthened shadow of many individuals—but often the individuals became better known than the enterprise. It was always characteristic of Battelle to keep to the background while its people gained prominence. This grew out of a tacit belief in the importance of the individual, an unquestioned assumption.

Another reason for the Institute's low visibility was its manner of conducting business: by means of contracts with industrial corporations and government, in which the customer received all of the benefits of research, including patents, as part of its recompense for supporting the Institute's efforts. The exciting and sometimes spectacular developments that stemmed from Battelle's work then became identified solely or almost solely with the sponsor.

The discoveries we made all along the way provided a stimulus that we had honestly not expected. The more we learned, the more there was to find out. Every positive thing we learned about Battelle seemed to pose as many questions as it answered. Finally, we became aware that we could not fully understand Battelle without also developing a greater comprehension of the interplay of science, society, and the human condition.

It has been an invigorating experience, and a satisfying one. This endless search, this reaching into the unknown, must be what makes scientists explore and writers write.

George A. W. Boehm
Alex Groner

New York
December 6, 1971

ance.

d individuals over
rying on a relent-
nst the billboard
would show an
e continued ex-
n the landscape,
unwillin ... t..
a hand in the

.ouraging progress
. due to the energy of
. department of public
.p a stretch of state high-
There also is a movement
the zoning ordinance so
be prohibited in certain

legislated against the
f cities have taken similar

. American institution and
.ime, a monument (although
..merican business enterprise.
.te years a number of leading
ve come to question the value of
'ertising, taking cognizance of the
feeling against their unsightli-
' large measure, any good will
for the advertiser.
1 out before, touring has
ime. The billboards inter-
form of recreation. They
' it deplorably and, not
hazards of motor travel.
ted. They are an evil, but

Our Sewage Disposal.

portant as the entire recon-
method of handling the city's
ie building of a new disposal
penditure of about $6,000,000,
ot hesitate, even at some ex-
omprehensive and reliable scien-
. on the problems involved.
'nvestigation of these matters
quire the setting up of a scien-
ouncil has already before it a
ced last week by Councilman
the appointment of a board
vestigate the different types of
iants and report upon the ef-
ind.
'ust be composed of chemists
professional standing, open-
'lisinterested. The resolu-
hat two of the three
council on recom-
mire, of Ohio State
t for granted that
.ot think for a mo-
chemists of the high-
mal ability and personal

be trusted as experts
. cost of installation,
atters of that nature;
relied upon with re-
wage plant, as tested
and sludge produced
this source that pol-
of the air we must

ure on these points, we
a trifling sum, when we
are to spend on the new
.ost of some bad blunder
o the new plant through
information.

nd this board of
speedily as pos-
o act without

experimental
of the most

Columbus Evening Dispatch

AN INDEPENDENT NEWSPAPER.

COLUMBUS EVENING DISPATCH, DAILY.
COLUMBUS SUNDAY DISPATCH, SUNDAY
THE DISPATCH PRINTING CO.

Publication Office: Dispatch Bldg., 34 S. Third St.

Entered at the Columbus, Ohio, post office as
second-class mail matter under act of congress.

MONDAY, JULY 21, 1930.

One of Our New Industries.

PERHAP. few of us appreciate the value)
Columbus of the service rendered by the
Battelle family in establishing the Battelle
Memorial Institute, the scientific work of which
was begun about a year ago, on completion of the
beautiful initial building, on West King avenue.
As the end of its first year of operation approaches, its payroll, all told, has only about
50 names; but in the course of the years to come,
it may mean more to the development of Columbus, even from the material point, of view, than
industries which number their employes by the
hundreds or thousands.
The reason why we say that it may mean
more is that the Battelle Institute is working on
basic problems, as yet unsolved, concerning the
properties of metals and other mineral substances
either already used in the arts and industries,
or possibly capable of being used to advantage,
after scientific research has more fully determined their properties and capabilities, either
alone or in combination with other substances
Such unsolved problems connected with mineral substances are of untold number, and
doubtless an army of scientists will be wrestling
with them for generations yet to come. Sometimes
such research suddenly hits upon a great discovery, utterly unforeseen, but of tremendous
importance in the further development of the
material and social phases of our civilization.
Such discoveries are welcomed when they come,
but in the usual course of things, the workers
in an institution like the Battelle Memorial render
their service to science and industry in a less
spectacular way, constantly adding bits of new
knowledge, at one point or another, which, as
the years go by, effect a steady and important
progress in man's task of learning the secrets of
nature and turning them into instrumentalities
of human welfare.
The Battelle Memorial Institute is well designed in its purpose, and so far as it has gone
it is accumulating the best of equipment for the
carrying out of that purpose. Its founders and
directors have wisely provided ample room for
the physical growth of the plant; and as its
character and purpose are more fully appreciated,
we have no doubt that far-seeing and public
spirited men of means, in Columbus and else-
where, will take pride in furnishing it with such
additional endowmen , or such special funds for
the working out of particular problems in research, as may from time to time be needed.
The time will come when scientists and indus-
trialists in many land will know of Columbus as
the home of the Battelle Memorial Institute.

Hugh

ELEPHANT
soft an
ailment
circus and z
go to work .
of life will b.
George De.
has been the .
long before he
phants to Englar.
elephants perhaps
country unless perhaps
Clark does, has strong ide.
"Trouble with elephan
trouble with human bei-
of them lead too soft .
logical park elephants
and out of condition,
long as they would :
hard, and take plenty
"I suppose son.eon.
like golf, so that the
keep in condition. F
the value of hard wi
healthy by watching e

"FINEST elephan
or African, i
that keep them
them in lifting
wagons. The el
to do the heav.
longer, grew big.
pler than those
because they work
didn't have time to
"Lots of lessons
I see Columbus has a
when you start gettir
keep them busy and wo
and haul, and lift and
bigger. You can't che
an African, but you
bigger. Keep ther
anything they war.
They'll eat better a
kept at work, and t
rather watch elephan
thing else. The bul
most of the time. Rec
they'd rather be at w
around.
"Look at most of the
They get fat, bleary eyed
soon they have boil-lik
their skin. They're just
get properous and don't
working, eat too much, tai.
get out of condition."
"I try to keep every r
herd exercising and wor'
but even then the lor
work leaves them too l

"COMPARE the zoo
some of the
much difference be
an athlete in tr:
fighter, and the
blocks walk to th
for a day.
"You'll find so
United States wi
There is old Tusl
bull has worked
the business. Bi
Tusky busy. He
in captivity ar
likes to work
the time; al
There is Ma
show, and '
animal an
enjoys life
"In th
all that w
the show.
the lot and
and grew fas
"When Ce
I'd say you c

CHAPTER ONE

Introducing Battelle

Late in 1929, as the Great Depression began, a staff of fewer than twenty scientists and engineers moved into a new brick and stone building of classical design in Columbus, Ohio. They had just been hired to provide a service that few, if any, prospective customers wanted at the time: industrial research. They had been instructed to carry out practical investigations of common metals, fuels, and allied industries in an endowed not-for-profit institution. They were also supposed to contribute to education, encourage inventions, and generally enhance the well-being of mankind. With this ambitious program, tiny Battelle Memorial Institute (BMI) first opened its doors.

All factors considered, if Battelle had been an ordinary business venture conducted by ordinary men, it should have been a fiasco, despite its liberal endowment of more than $3.5 million. If Battelle had been a publicly owned corporation, a shrewd investor might have mortgaged his home to sell the stock short with a reasonable expectation of making a fortune.

Yet from unpropitious beginnings, the Institute has grown and flourished with hardly a setback. Today it ranks among the most successful ventures of any kind in recent decades.

No matter how it is viewed, Battelle is big and healthy and also wealthy. As an array of industrial laboratories with more than 5,500 people, it is larger than any except the Bell Telephone Laboratories. As a center of science and engineering discovery, it is as active as the University of Illinois. As a foundation of the

1

Battelle Memorial Institute is organized under Ohio state law as a not-for-profit corporation. A not-for-profit organization may properly have net gain (earnings) from its operations so long as no part of such gain is distributed to members, officers, or other persons. Hence, a not-for-profit organization cannot pay any dividends, bonuses, or other amounts to trustees, officers, employees, or other individuals. Thus it is proper, and in some years occurs, that Battelle has a net gain from its operations. Any such net gain must be utilized for the purposes for which Battelle was organized, e.g., for such things as the acquisition and replacement of facilities and equipment and such other expenses and capital items as are necessary to carry out research and educational purposes.

Battelle and its components pay state and local real estate, sales, and tangible personal property tax, etc. Battelle is, however, exempt from federal corporate income tax under Section 501(c)(3) because: (1) it has scientific and educational purposes, (2) no part of any net gain accrues to the benefit of any private individual, and (3) it refrains from certain prohibited activities under the federal statute, such as carrying on propaganda, participating in political campaigns, etc.

Although not a point of law or statute, Battelle has determined as a matter of policy that it will not engage in those activities which are described under the various state statutes covering the practice of professional engineering, by either individuals or organizations.

Ford or Rockefeller type, it is among the first ten in the country. As an independent not-for-profit research institute (the accurate classification), it is almost as big and as busy as the next ten combined. If it were regarded as an industrial corporation, it would come close to making the *Fortune* list of the top 500 U.S. companies. In comparison with most business enterprises, it has been a bonanza. Its assets of laboratories and other buildings, equipment, land, and invested capital now have a market value about 100 times as great as the original endowment. The short-seller would long ago have lost his shirt.

Spreading the Gospel of Research

Battelle has other accomplishments to its credit—broader and less readily measurable than its exceptional growth but even more significant. While doing well, it has done good. It has, for example, set the style for nonprofit research institutes, which have been proliferating, especially since the end of World War II. In fact, Battelle men served as midwives in the birth of several and were appointed to their boards of directors.

The same is true of some of today's leading industrial labora-tories. Until the mid-1940s few corporate laboratories did much more than routine testing. Battelle showed several of its clients how to set up their own research laboratories, some of which were headed by Battelle alumni. Establishing competition proved not to be a strategic blunder, for the growth of sophisticated research organizations appreciably sharpened the nation's appetite for sci-ence and engineering and greatly increased the market for Bat-telle's services. Earl Hayes, chief scientist of the U.S. Bureau of Mines, sums up Battelle's influence thus: "They were the first to understand that research can be managed and to show how to manage it."

For such a large and influential organization, the Institute has always managed with a remarkably light hand. Long-range master plans have been drawn up from time to time, but until the last few years they were not followed closely. As one of the old-timers put it: "We always knew we could do anything we wanted, within our overall guidelines, so long as it worked out well." This laissez-faire policy is extended to dealings with companies and govern-ment agencies who have sponsored projects at Battelle. The client,

A Chronology of Battelle's Top Managers

Battelle has had only four chief operating executives since opening its doors in 1929. They have been: Horace Gillett, 1929–34; Clyde Williams, 1934–57; Bert Thomas, 1957–68; and Sherwood Fawcett, 1968—. For more than twenty years the top operating executive held the title of Director of Battelle Memorial Institute. The Presidency was a more or less honorary post held by a member of the Board of Trustees.

Then in 1952, with Battelle growing rapidly and expanding into Europe, Williams requested the Board to give him the additional title of President. The Board agreed, and since that time the chief operating executive has been designated as President.

When the European laboratories were well established in 1954, each got its own Director: Hugo Thiemann at Battelle-Geneva and Max Barnick at Battelle-Frankfurt. They still hold those positions.

In 1958, when Thomas was named President, he named David Minton Director of the Columbus Laboratories (BCL). Minton was succeeded in 1970 by Roger Merrill, the current Director.

The Pacific Northwest Division, often identified as Battelle-Northwest (BNW), was established in 1964 with the acquisition of the management contract for the Atomic Energy Commission's Hanford Laboratories and was later augmented by the opening of the Seattle Research Center. Both facilities are under one Director. The first to hold this post was Sherwood Fawcett. When he returned to Columbus, he was succeeded by Fred Albaugh in 1967 and by Ronald Paul in 1970.

or sponsor, has always bypassed layers of management to deal directly with the engineer or scientist doing the job. One sponsor who has engaged Battelle on and off for thirty years says: "I really appreciate knowing the man who is running my project, not just the guy who signed the contract."

One reason the Institute has thrived with light management has been the high concentration of able people on the staff through the years. This was most conspicuously true in the early days, when the extent of industrial research anywhere was limited. Battelle could, and often did, hire two or three outstanding men and thereby become preeminent overnight in some emerging field.

A Little Ahead of the Times

The Institute also reflects the diverse talents of the four men who have in turn served as director. Each had a style peculiarly appropriate to his time. Each endeavored to keep Battelle a little ahead in fields that seemed important—but not so far ahead as to lose touch with practical problems of the day.

The first was Horace Gillett, who combined an encyclopedic knowledge of metallurgy with a loathing of the slightest sloppiness or pretentiousness. But Gillett hated administration and promotion so much that in 1934 he insisted on exchanging jobs with his assistant director, Clyde Williams. Williams was just the man to push ahead with growth, more growth, and still more growth. While highly respected in technical circles, he also had the charm, the zeal, and the appreciation of economics to convince company presidents and board chairmen that they needed Battelle. Among other accomplishments, he firmly established the Institute abroad, with major laboratories in Frankfurt and Geneva.

After Williams, with his genius for expanding income, came Bert Thomas, who had a flare for spending it imaginatively for worthwhile purposes. Under Thomas, a scientist-philosopher, the Institute branched out laterally into a multitude of new fields and for the first time established close ties with the academic community. He also arranged for Battelle to acquire a fourth major laboratory: part of the Atomic Energy Commission's (AEC) Hanford Works in Richland, Washington.

When Thomas retired in 1968, he was succeeded by Sherwood Fawcett, a nuclear physicist interested in finally structuring Bat-

5

telle's catch-as-catch-can administrative methods. He is also intent on further diversification, especially wherever the scientific approach is particularly relevant to social problems.

"Relevance" has in many circles become a vague catchword, often used to damn basic research. At the same time some of the same people condemn much of technical progress because of pollution and other side effects. Fawcett explains the implications for Battelle's future in this succinct way: "We need to design our industrial system to optimize the Earth's closed system. The price or value of products must include the cost of production under conditions that do not adversely affect the environment. This is a new challenge for science and technology."

The individual styles and accomplishments of these four leaders will be examined in detail in Chapter Eleven.

Through a process of evolution Battelle has filled a gap between the universities and the industrial laboratories. The Institute, and some of the other independents, probe more deeply into practical applications of science and technology than university groups can or care to do. Whereas most industrial laboratories are constrained to develop or improve products that will soon prove profitable, Battelle's diversification equips it to enter hybrid fields such as oceanology or the overall planning of regional transportation— high-risk, long-term, multidisciplinary programs that very few industries even consider.

Ready for Almost Anything

There was never time, money, or brainpower to excel throughout the enormous range of modern science and technology. In retrospect, staff members sometimes regret that they missed certain good bets such as the early stages of computer design and application or pioneer work in solid-state electronics.

Nevertheless, a sampling of projects currently under way suggests how broadly Battelle has expanded its interests and capabilities since the early days. Mostly diversification has come about because one or a few enthusiastic researchers have found a new interest and pursued it until their ideas could be made valuable to sponsors. To list only a handful of hundreds of ongoing or recent projects:

○ Analysis of the new San Francisco Bay Area rapid transit system from the safety viewpoint.

6

- Creation of a nutritionally balanced food from unused or little-used byproducts of the milling, food processing, brewing, and pharmaceutical industries.
- A worldwide study of the state of the art in the conversion of salt water to fresh water.
- Advancement of a concept for using plasmas to produce electrical energy that would greatly reduce pollution.
- Evaluation of thousands of chemicals that may work against cancer.
- Development of a device employing electromagnetic energy to detect concealed weapons in air terminal boarding areas.
- Planning an optimal economic strategy for replacing or renovating housing on U.S. Navy bases.
- A study using network analysis to identify the most efficient and economic plan for construction of a major air freight terminal.
- Perfecting machinery to enable the U.S. Post Office to sort 90 percent of all mail automatically, more cheaply, and much faster.
- The building of a smog-generating chamber to study problems of air pollution.
- Improvements to incinerators to enable them to burn more material with less pollution.
- Development of a system that provides continuous rapid passenger transport on conveyor belts in urban areas.
- Publication of an analysis of Soviet space science.
- The design of drugs with effects that can be predicted theoretically from their molecular architecture.
- Preparation of ceramic teeth to be implanted in human jaws; they are now being tested on laboratory animals.
- Study of uses and markets for Brazilian coal.

While growing, and finding new outlets for research, Battelle has maintained its traditional position in mining and metallurgy. In fact, it seems to be doing better than ever, according to Nathan Promisel. As an administrator of materials science first with the U.S. Navy and then with the National Academy of Sciences, he has seen Battelle mature since about 1940. In his opinion: "The good old days were really not so good as the good new days."

7

Despite its solid reputation among those who have dealt with it over the years, Battelle has never gained nearly the wide public recognition that its accomplishments merit. The chief reason is that, aside from technical papers written by the staff, most of the advances that the Institute generates belong to its sponsors, who naturally enough take most of the publicity for themselves.

Perhaps Battelle needs a catchy slogan. One has indeed been proposed by John Wheeler, a renowned physicist at Princeton who is a member of the Battelle Board of Trustees. Though known primarily as a lofty theoretician, Wheeler admires down-to-earth research and suggests that Battelle deserves the following motto: "The best thinking in the service of the greatest issues."

CHAPTER TWO

Family and Founding

To many who knew him, Gordon Battelle seemed an unlikely person to conceive and found one of the world's great technological institutions. True, he had studied some metallurgy at Yale University's Sheffield Scientific School, but he was hardly more than a scientific onlooker. Born August 10, 1883, he grew up in a world of turn-of-the-century affluence—elegant home, good food and drink, prep school, and travel.

But Gordon Battelle had a Calvinistic streak that drove him toward some achievement worthy of his family—a trait that seemed firmly embedded in the bloodline. The Battelles were of British (and probably Norman) origin. Thomas Battelle was a member of the Massachusetts Bay Colony and his name was entered on the rolls at Dedham, Massachusetts in 1648. His great grandson, Ebenezer, served as a captain in the Revolutionary forces.

The branch of the family that was to become prominent in the development of industry in Ohio was started by Ebenezer Battelle, Jr., great-great grandson of Thomas. After graduating from Harvard in 1774, he served as a volunteer under his father at Lexington, and subsequently became a colonel of militia. When the Ohio Company was formed to purchase and develop a huge tract of land north of the Ohio River, Colonel Battelle became one of its agents. With his father, he left Boston with the company's second colonizing group in 1788 for the new settlement of Marietta, Ohio.

The Colonel's grandson, the Reverend Gordon Battelle, served as a chaplain in the Union Army during the Civil War. It was his

9

son, John Gordon Battelle, who built the substantial fortune that was eventually to provide the endowment for Battelle Memorial Institute. At the age of 21, he became secretary and general superintendent of the Norway Manufacturing Company of Wheeling. A few years later he organized a new enterprise, J. G. Battelle and Company, at Memphis. He married Annie Maude Norton there in 1881, and two years later they moved back to Ohio, settling first in Cincinnati, then in Piqua. He went into the sheet metal business with Joseph H. Frantz. After they sold out, with the agreement that they would not return to the business for a time, they set up a blast furnace in Columbus in 1905. Well financed, they were able to keep production steady by stocking inventory in bad times and selling when prices rose. When the Block brothers decided to expand from the scrap iron business to form a new steel company in Chicago, they came to Colonel Battelle (the rank had been conferred on him by the governor of Ohio) for help. He agreed to sign their note for $200,000 in exchange for stock in their new Inland Steel Company. In 1917 he and Frantz sold their Columbus Iron & Steel Works to the American Rolling Mill Company—which has been Armco Steel Corporation since 1948. When Battelle died in 1918, the bulk of his estate of more than $1.5 million was left to his wife and his son, Gordon.

The Ozark Mines

Some zinc-mining land in the Ozarks, near Joplin, Missouri, purchased by Frantz and Colonel Battelle as a source of galvanizing metal, had become a kind of family joke because of the poor quality of the ores. It was here that Gordon Battelle felt that he might make his mark—or at least impress his father's friends—if he could derive some economic value from those ores.

Although zinc was plentiful in the mines, it was chemically tied up in such a way that it could not be recovered by simple roasting. Gordon Battelle consulted metallurgists from Ohio State University, and went on to seek help from Arthur D. Little, Inc., where Earl Stevenson went to work on the problem. In the Joplin area, he met W. George Waring, a scientist and former professor, then trying to find a way to make zinc tailings and mine water commercially valuable. He built a small laboratory for Waring. Stevenson worked out a process of treating the ores with ammonia and ammonium sulfate to produce a double ammonium-zinc sulphate salt that could be roasted, and Waring worked on the commercial application of the process. A patent was obtained.

At the same time, Stevenson was tutoring Gordon Battelle, seeking to upgrade his knowledge of chemistry. A willing student, Battelle also talked eagerly about pushing the patent and making something of it. And while he remained a dilettante in science, he expressed great enthusiasm about the good that research could accomplish in industry.

The idea began to be something of an obsession with Battelle. Industry in those days relied largely on handing down its knowledge and skills from one generation to another, and industrial research was relatively new. The General Electric Company, shortly after its organization, established the first permanent industrial research laboratory around 1900. By 1915 there were only about 100 industrial laboratories in the country, most of them limited to routine, repetitive testing.

Gordon Battelle spent more and more of his time thinking and talking about his idea—in his office on Broad Street in Columbus, riding about in his chauffeur-driven limousine, visiting with and talking to friends and associates. A neighbor, Austin McElroy, recalls: "Gordon would get steamed up and go on talking about it until my wife would say, 'I'm going out to the kitchen to get a glass of water,' and she'd disappear. He would talk on and on, but I had to go to work in the morning, even if he didn't. He didn't have to go to his office, but he went. Gordon was in no sense a playboy. He was a man of serious purpose."

Gordon Battelle never did establish his industrial research laboratory. He died on September 21, 1923, at the age of forty, following an appendectomy. Yet his strong sense of mission caused him to embody the idea in his will, which left the bulk of his estate to the establishment of a "Battelle Memorial Institute."

Providing for the Institute

Precisely what kind of institution Gordon Battelle had in mind is difficult to ascertain today. The will covered specifically those areas of industrial research with which he was himself most familiar, but was couched in language broad enough to provide for maximum flexibility. Certainly, had he lived he would have established his laboratory. The period after World War I was a time when many Americans, especially those whose backgrounds were like Battelle's, saw a close identity between the advancement of industry and the betterment of the human condition.

Some felt that his principal idea was to found an institute that would emphasize the development and application of patents, possibly through licensing. Others felt that education should be a principal objective. But it was McElroy's impression that Battelle showed a greater concern for the advancement of knowledge than for the practical application of research. Still others believed that the Arthur D. Little organization was his model, although ADL was a profit-making business venture. Stevenson himself believed that the basic idea was the establishment of a regional laboratory to serve the heavy industries of the Midwest. And many others feel that what he had in mind was another Mellon Institute, which started to sponsor industrial fellowships on a nonprofit basis at the University of Pittsburgh in 1913. In 1927 Mellon cut its ties with the university and incorporated as the first of the independent industrial research groups. The fellowship program, however, is quite different from the industry-sponsored, staff-executed research project that has been Battelle's main activity.

Gordon Battelle was well aware of the Mellon Institute, and mentioned it to the people with whom he spoke. But the likelihood was that he was trying to create something totally new, something

12

that did not exist at the time. He sensed that industry, and smaller industrial companies in particular, had a pressing need for research help that was then not available from universities, industrial laboratories, or the existing research organizations.

"Item Twenty-First" of his will was the clause that provided for the establishment of the new Institute. "All the residue of my estate . . . ," it declared, "I give . . . for the foundation of a 'Battelle Memorial Institute,' to be established . . . for the purpose of education in connection with and the encouragement of creative and research work and the making of discoveries and inventions in connection with the metallurgy of coal, iron, steel, zinc and their allied industries . . . ."

The clause provided for a Board of Trustees who "shall undertake and assist in the discovery of such new experiments and processes and license or dispose of the same in such manner and upon such terms as may seem advisable for the continuance and advancement of said 'Battelle Memorial Institute' and the purposes for which it was founded."

Establishing the Institute

The simple statement of faith in scientific research and innovation, so commonplace today, was relatively novel when Battelle included it in his will. That he thought the idea one of great importance is shown in his choice of the members of the Board of Trustees, named in the will:

○ Bishop John W. Hamilton, a relative and at the time president of American University in Washington, D.C.;

○ Warren G. Harding, then President-elect of the United States, a friend of Gordon Battelle and of his mother;

○ Annie Norton Battelle, Gordon's mother;

○ Earl Clark Derby, a Columbus industrialist;

○ Joseph H. Frantz, Colonel Battelle's onetime partner; and

○ Harry M. Runkle, a Columbus lawyer and business associate.

President Harding had already died when Annie Norton Battelle passed away on March 23, 1925, leaving $2,172,000—most of her estate—to the institute her son had created. With this bequest, the

13

total sum available for the founding of the new institute was more than $3.5 million, an impressive amount for such a purpose in those times.

The four surviving trustees, and a fifth, Gerald Fenton, appointed by the others, established Battelle Memorial Institute as a not-for-profit corporation on March 27, 1925. Fenton was a cousin of Gordon Battelle, some ten years his junior, and a business manager for American Rolling Mill Company. His superior in that job was Joseph Frantz, who subsequently asked Fenton to join the new Institute as its business manager. Indeed, much of the credit for the form taken by the Institute and for the soundness of its organization must go to Frantz, who became Chairman of the Board at the time of incorporation and held that post until his death in 1938.

The residues of the two estates were not finally distributed to Battelle Memorial Institute until March 1, 1927. Since a good part of the assets were in industrial stocks, the Institute's account benefited from the rising market. In 1928 Frantz thought that the Inland, Republic Steel, and American Rolling Mill stock was overpriced, and the trustees agreed that this part of the portfolio should be sold and the proceeds put into government bonds—something that was done in time to avoid the 1929 crash.

The trustees then set about putting up a building on a ten-acre site they had purchased, and hiring the initial staff. Construction began with the King Avenue Building, later called Building A. The first part of the building was completed in 1929, and by September of that year both the north section and west wing were up.

While it was well stocked with good business judgment, the original board was weak in scientific background. Not one of the trustees had a speaking acquaintanceship with science, or even much appreciation of its applications to industry. Nonetheless, they made some excellent staff choices. The first appointed Director of the Institute was Gerald Wendt, a University of Chicago professor who was later to become editor of *Science Illustrated,* but he left after some differences with the trustees. Next invited to take charge was the Chief of the Metallurgical Division of the National Bureau of Standards, Horace Gillett, who had once worked with Thomas Edison. The trustees did not know quite what to make of him at the start. He came off the train looking disheveled, in an old sweater, carrying a battered suitcase, and reeking of stale pipe tobacco. But they were soon completely taken by the manner and charm of this incredibly knowledgeable man, and hired him at a salary of $10,000 a year, which was twice what he had been getting.

It was probably the best bargain the Board ever made, and Gillett soon set about staffing the Institute with some of the leading metallurgists in the nation. There was a staff of twenty when the Institute opened in the summer of 1929. That September Gillett and Fenton hired a young mechanical engineer named William Welcker, who was before many more years to take charge of all of Battelle's physical facilities, including the sprawling complex of buildings—at least one of which he designed, when the original design man left.

By the end of 1929, Battelle Memorial Institute was a going proposition, although not yet quite certain just where it was going or how it would get there.

CHAPTER THREE

Off to a Running Start

Almost from the beginning, a truly remarkable concentration of talent enabled Battelle to surmount the two main obstacles confronting it: hard times and industry's indifference to research. Gillett—soon aided by Williams, whom he brought from the U.S. Bureau of Mines—started at once to recruit a select group of experts in metals and fuels. They had known and worked with most of them at the National Bureau of Standards or the Bureau of Mines. Within a few years, when the professional staff numbered less than fifty, the Institute could rightly claim that a list of the ten best metallurgists in the United States would include at least five on the staff of Battelle.

What Arthur Murray was to ballroom dancing, Escoffier was to *haute cuisine,* and Emily Post was to social graces, Gillett was to metallurgy. Though inventive in his own right, he spent less and less time in the laboratory and the foundry so that he could devote more and more attention to setting high standards for Battelle and keeping them high. Long the editor of the authoritative journal *Metals and Alloys,* he had a broader view of his subject than any man of his time. For years, up to his retirement in early 1949, he read almost every serious book or article published about metals, including all reports and proposals emanating from Battelle.

Regarding Battelle's output, Gillett was both judge and jury. He read a page at a glance, but he seldom missed the slightest inaccuracy or even clumsiness of style. The author of a report usually got it back from Gillett the next day, often with a pithy comment ranging from "splendid report" to "this looks like a lot of hog-wash to me." Frequently Gillett undertook heavy editing to correct facts, grammar, and style. Occasionally his own wry sense of humor showed through. When a researcher had written blandly: "There is no tin in Ireland," Gillett changed it to read: "In Ireland tin is scarce as snakes." Sloppy writing disgusted him. Bruce Gonser, one of the early metallurgists later famous for his work on titanium, recalls that Gillett once called him in to discuss a report prepared by one of Gonser's subordinates. Gillett slapped the report down on the desk and said to Gonser: "You wouldn't write this badly yourself. Why do you let your man get away with it?"

Some Early Giants

The men who joined Battelle in the early 1930s were a diverse lot of personalities. Among the first was Howard Russell—red-headed, impetuous, a floor-pacer, a chain smoker. He would barge into a room, flinging the door open so hard that the doorknob would dent the wall. Trained as a physicist, Russell was confident that the long-range future of metallurgy lay in explaining phenomena such as hardness and tensile strength in terms of basic physical principles, and indeed this represents the nature of modern metallurgy.

Then there was John Sullivan, one of the first of the chemists, who helped establish Battelle as a center for research in ceramics. One of his associates describes him as a "St. Patrick's day Irishman," and recalls: "He was a holy terror who could not keep a secretary till he got an Irish girl with a temper to match his own." At the same time, almost anonymously, he helped finance the educations of several young men.

At the opposite extreme was Bert Thomas (later Director and President), a quiet, scholarly man who wore his bushy hair long before the mod look came into style. Though hired for his skill in accounting as well as for his doctoral training in chemistry, Thomas took little interest in the early business meetings. He often sat through them filling a pad with symbols of abstract mathematics, one of his lifelong hobbies.

Another low-key individual was Oscar Harder, a former university professor who after 1934 served as an administrative assistant to Clyde Williams. He was proud of having been born in a log cabin and largely having educated himself up to the college level. He made a point of getting to know new staff members, and he "mothered" many a young man through the confusion of the first few weeks on the job.

The Hard, Easy-Going Days

At the beginning and for several years after, Battelle staff members in their off hours behaved much like members of a social club. Every month all of them with their wives assembled for a party. While the crowd was still small, Harder presided over the steak grill; later the food was brought in by a caterer. After dinner most of the men adjourned to the library for low-stakes poker, while their wives played bridge or chatted in nearby rooms.

The same sort of informality extended through working hours. Until the 1940s, when the staff grew beyond 200, everyone was on a first-name basis with everyone else. Officially, working hours were five and a half days a week, but when a man felt so inclined he would take the afternoon off to play golf or go hunting. Almost without exception, however, the researchers averaged a good deal more than five and a half days a week. Many preferred to work nights and weekends. Indeed, an informal meeting was held every Sunday morning in the library, with most of the top men present to discuss their problems and get advice.

Through most of the first decade the engineers and scientists also had to be expert plumbers, electricians, and sheet metal workers, for technicians were scarce. George Krumlauf, who arrived at Battelle as a foundry worker in 1937, recalls: "I learned to fire every furnace in the place—mostly from Clarence Sims and Clarence Lorig, two of the top metallurgists, who were never too proud to put on coveralls and grab a shovel." Krumlauf, who never went to college, also acquired the equivalent of an excellent technical education from his bosses and eventually became a sales executive for Republic Steel. When he asked a question, he usually got an answer—not just a sentence or two but often an informative discussion that might take two or three hours. He credits his learning chiefly to Lorig, Sims, Gillett, Sullivan, and Williams, who taught him as a master craftsman would teach an apprentice. Sullivan,

19

despite his natural impatience, was among the best teachers, al-though, according to Krumlauf, "he would burst into a rage if he thought you were just trying to impress him or butter him up."

Early Battelle had a few other technicians who made major contributions. Sullivan gratefully recalls the help he got from Charlie Raab, who headed the machine shop and could make almost anything needed. Other old-timers feel they owe a special debt to "Pop" Smith, a technician in mineral dressing, who would build machines from sketches drawn on the floor.

Bread and Butter from Steel

In its first years the Institute tended to concentrate research on iron and steel. Shortly after he was hired in 1931, Lorig was as-signed to help the Worthington Pump Company build a pump that would withstand exceptionally high temperatures. He succeeded by adding a little molybdenum to the steel used in making a critical valve. "This project," says Lorig, "was typical of the early days. Problems were clearly defined and had objective solutions."

Lorig also had a hand in developing a new kind of low-alloy corrosion-resistant steel. The basic idea, which originated partly at Battelle, was to reduce rusting through the addition of a little phos-phorus. As every experienced steelmaker knew at the time, phos-phorus in steel can be impractical, because it tends to make the metal brittle. But Lorig and his associates found out that this brittleness could be offset by reducing the carbon content roughly in proportion to the amount of phosphorus added. The result was a kind of structural steel that has become increasingly popular in architecture for unpainted exterior columns, walls, and roofs. It develops a skin-deep rich brown patina but does not rust deeply enough to become weakened.

When Sims arrived in 1936 the direct, largely empirical approach still prevailed. He was given the task of making steel easier to machine. A predecessor had tried the Edison approach, adding a bit of this or a trace of that—whatever was at hand—to small sam-ples of molten steel, and when he quit, he left behind twenty-nine small billets with notes on what each one contained. Sims tried machining the billets and found that two had excellent properties. Referring to the notes, he learned that both contained a little type-metal—an alloy of lead, antimony, and arsenic. After six months of further work, he pinned down the fact that it was the lead in the type-metal that was important and found out just how much lead gave the best results.

Shortly thereafter Sims went to work on a contract sponsored by Alcoa, which was looking for ways to sell aluminum to the steel industry. It was thought that the addition of a little aluminum might reduce the porosity of steel castings. The first trials produced erratic results: the steel was less porous but it was also too brittle. Then Sims, working partly on hunch and partly on theory, added more and more aluminum. Finally he reached a point where the steel was no longer porous or brittle. As Sims remembers, "The stipend for the work was $500 a month. I got so hot on it that I spent six months of support money in two months, and I got hell from the sponsor."

It was not unusual in those days for the sponsor to keep careful watch over a few hundred dollars, nor was it unusual for the sponsor to accept results and disregard the rest of a report explaining the underlying theories. Most of the people who contracted for research at Battelle knew exactly what they wanted and said, in effect, "Don't tell me why; just tell me how."

Battelle scored many other triumphs in steel research. One that paid off immediately was a search for a better alloy for watch-springs, for the Elgin Watch Company. Harder and D. A. Roberts developed Elgiloy, which resisted corrosion and fatigue, the tendency of metals to become brittle when flexed repeatedly.

Through projects such as these, the Institute developed leadership in solving problems found in working with many ferrous alloys and other metals. The tendency of traces of hydrogen to make metals brittle was explored. Battelle became the national center for testing "creep," the permanent deformation of metals exposed to stress and heat over long periods of time. And several researchers became authorities on fatigue, which in later years became a matter of public concern when some airplanes came apart in midair.

Invention of Contract Research

By 1934, when Williams became Director, Battelle was almost in the black. Until then each year Gillett had had to ask the Board to dip into the endowment to help pay expenses. The Trustees came through every time, although one of them, a conservative Ohio industrialist, grumbled about entrusting so much money to "irresponsible scientists."

The key to Battelle's growth was the concept of contract research, work undertaken for a specific sponsor under a kind of cost-plus arrangement. Williams pushed contract research, foreseeing that it would provide funds for the Institute to grow indefinitely. He also had a hand in drawing up the first contract blanks; though the forms were modified from time to time, the one in use today is not much different from that devised in the early 1930s.

In brief, the provisions are as follows: Battelle agrees to undertake a specific research project, whose goals are carefully described. The starting and finishing dates are inserted. The sponsor is committed to pay for staff costs, materials, equipment, travel, and overhead, with the total not to exceed a stipulated amount. The information to be developed or found, including patentable discoveries, belongs to the sponsor. The Institute is not allowed to disclose results of the research without the sponsor's consent. On the other hand, the sponsor agrees not to exploit Battelle's name and reputation in advertising, sales promotion, or publicity without the Institute's permission.

Battelle does not guarantee success; it just promises to do its level best. Oddly enough, the fact that they may be getting nothing worth having has never discouraged many sponsors. Around 1934 Williams and Thomas visited the president of a large company and persuaded him to sponsor a sizable research project. Before signing, the president called in his chief lawyer, who read the contract and said: "This piece of paper doesn't mean a damned thing legally. Just the same, I advise you to sign it."

And so it is today that sponsors realize they are not buying a product but rather betting on Battelle's reputation for skill and honesty. Though such a deal is uncommon in the business world, it is not unlike the unwritten agreement between a physician and his patient. The doctor doesn't promise a cure, although the patient expects him to try hard. Moreover, the fee does not depend on the success of the treatment.

Every Man an Entrepreneur

For the staff, the growing success of contract research opened up prospects of advancement through exploiting their own ideas. If a man generated an idea that a sponsor would support, he was likely to get the backing of the Director—likely but not certain. At the top, Battelle had a strict conscience.

Gillett once vetoed a vague proposal that a prospective sponsor actually suggested: to try to improve certain properties of steel plate by adding some molybdenum or other exotic metals. Gillett judged it a pointless "fishing expedition" with little chance of success. Some years afterward, Hugo Johnson (now president of the American Iron Ore Association) had a sponsor ready to sign a $1 million contract, one of the most lucrative projects up to that time. Williams, who had taken over as Director, expressed doubt that the research would come to anything, and he insisted that it be broken down into three stages. After each of the first two a full report would be made so that the sponsor could be warned to discontinue the program if its promise dwindled.

In most cases, however, projects that were well conceived and energetically promoted found sponsors. Thus each leading man became a sort of small-scale income-producing center within the Institute. If he had enough good research ideas and could get them sponsored, he quickly rose to be a division head.

Some researchers staked out specialties in which they became national authorities. One of the earliest contracts—Number Four—was signed jointly by four iron-mining companies who wanted to investigate the feasibility of concentrating low-grade ores so they could be used for making iron. Byron Bird, later joined by A. C.

Richardson, started an ore-dressing laboratory, and for several years the physical concentration of ores was a major activity for Battelle.

Ralph Sherman, who had worked on fuels and combustion at the Bureau of Mines, oversaw a procession of contracts dealing with powdered coal. Technically, his work was brilliantly successful, resulting in numerous uses for pulverized coal in locomotives, home furnaces, and under pressure in gas turbine heaters. But in time competition from oil and gas became overwhelming.

Even newcomers soon came to understand that having a sponsorable specialty was to their advantage. When Bruce Gonser was hired in 1934, he was already an accomplished metallurgist with a doctorate from Harvard and some experience in industry. Seeing all the good work already in progress at Battelle, he made the conscious decision to specialize in nonferrous metals. Beginning with copper, he branched out to zirconium and other exotics. Before 1940 Gonser and other nonferrous metallurgists had made at least a cursory study of every metal in the periodic table of the elements. These intellectual adventures eventually proved extremely significant to Battelle, for they prepared the Institute to take a leading role in research on little-known materials for atomic energy and also high-performance jet engines. As early as 1935 Thomas had suggested that Battelle support fairly extensive research of its own on titanium. Gillett turned him down, saying: "You're ten years too early." Sure enough, not until about 1946 did titanium become the glamour metal of the early postwar years.

Without much planned diversification, one thing led to another, and before the end of its first decade the Institute was doing work in many areas of research and development.

Branching Out

In the first stages of the Depression, a trade association of copper producers contracted with Battelle to discover new uses for copper. This continuing program was largely responsible for the Institute's first burst of diversification.

Researchers soon discovered the importance of copper as a trace element in soil. Pinning down its nutritional effects on plants led them into agricultural chemistry. They also developed copper-based paints and chemicals to protect ship bottoms, piers, and swimming pools from marine organisms that devoured wood or deposited slime. This work got them into oceanology with a modest test facility near Daytona Beach, Florida. Improvements in copper printing plates were the takeoff point for a large division devoted to graphic arts.

The copper producers also wanted to dispose profitably of selenium, then a useless byproduct of refining. Battelle chemists, working with biologists, devised an insecticide that could be applied around the roots of plants. It was too toxic for use around food plants, but it gave excellent protection to ornamentals. During the course of this research, the men in charge of the project bought an abandoned greenhouse, dismantled it, and reassembled it on Battelle property. This led one of the Trustees to inquire: "What in hell are we doing with a goddamned conservatory?"

Indeed, toward the end of the 1930s the Institute was expanding into new areas so rapidly that even Gillett was hard pressed to keep up with all that was happening. In addition to the work already mentioned, some of the researchers had become top authorities on methods of depositing metals either from decomposition of vapors or by electrolysis. Another Battelle specialty, directed by Charles Faust, was electropolishing, a method of immersing a roughly polished piece of metal in a solution and then subjecting it to an electric current which gradually eroded the microscopic high points until the surface was gleamingly smooth.

In one odd partnership, the nation's leading producer of playing cards and the largest publisher of bibles jointly sponsored a research contract on applying gilt to the edges of paper or cardboard. The process that resulted was not suitable for gilding thin pages, but it worked well for playing cards.

While concentrating on the physical and biological sciences and technologies, Battelle began to get its feet wet in the social sciences. As Lorig puts it: "Engineers did economics on the fly." That is to say, a man expert in steel or copper metallurgy could be persuaded to project the demand and identify future markets for certain ores, products, or byproducts. By today's standards the reports were unsophisticated, but, because they were done by men who kept up with technical literature and talked shop with other thoughtful specialists, some of them held up well for several years.

The most prophetic of these broad surveys was written by Gillett himself, with the aid of Williams. In 1937, after studying German technical literature, Gillett wrote an editorial for *Metals and Alloys* predicting imminent war in Europe. Later, when war did break out and the United States seemed likely to become involved, Gillett and Williams drew up a detailed plan for the metallurgical research the U.S. would soon be needing. This report can be said to have wrapped up the first decade of Battelle's existence and paved the way to a new era.

CHAPTER FOUR

Wartime and Postwar Growth

When war did break out and the United States decided to become the arsenal of democracy, Battelle was ready to lead the search for the new materials needed. The Institute had established its expertise in the problems of common metals and their alloys. Its occasional studies of such uncommon metals as titanium and zirconium had given it a virtual monopoly in the knowledge of exotic materials that were to prove vital. Moreover, it could provide a pool of men skilled in organizing and managing big research projects under time pressure.

The first federal government contract in Battelle's history was signed in 1939: a U.S. Army project on the improvement of armor plate. The Institute agreed to do the work at cost, and several more contracts were undertaken on similar terms. Soon, though, it became obvious that the volume of war research was becoming so great that the usual markup would have to be charged.

Nevertheless, Battelle continued to contribute freely the advice and managerial skill of many of its top men. The director himself, Clyde Williams, in effect took a leave of absence to head the War Metallurgy Committee (WMC), spending at least two days a week in Washington.

The WMC was near the top of the hierarchy of wartime science and engineering, whose achievements did much to awaken the American public to the importance of technology. The top level was the Office of Scientific Research and Development, bossed by Vannevar Bush of MIT. Immediately down the line was the

National Defense Research Committee (NDRC), headed by James Conant, president of Harvard. The WMC was Division 18 of NDRC. Williams was the administrative chief of the WMC. Zay Jeffries, a General Electric vice-president and later chairman of the Battelle Board of Trustees, was in charge of technical work. Sullivan headed research on materials, Vernon Schnee on products. In addition to these, the senior staff included several others from Battelle: Gillett, Gonser, Lorig, Howard Cross, and Dave Minton.

The achievements made under the WMC are too numerous to list, but they included: aluminum and magnesium alloys for aircraft frames; high-temperature alloys for gas turbine ship engines and airplane jet engines; welded steel ships; and a continuing surveillance of German and Japanese materials. Back in Columbus, Battelle carried out many of the WMC research programs.

Writing the Book on Uranium

The Institute also played a major role in the Manhattan District of the U.S. Army Corps of Engineers, as the atomic bomb program was then known. Howard Russell headed Battelle's effort, which eventually involved 400 staff members (twice as many people as the total employed in Columbus at the beginning of the war). A veteran Atomic Energy Commission research administrator recalls that Russell and his staff "wrote the book on uranium metallurgy, including rolling, extrusion, and wire drawing." He also remembers Russell's participation in the monthly top-level scientific meetings: "When he disagreed with what was being discussed, he would clear his throat loudly and bellow in his foghorn voice, 'Now, just hold on a minute . . . .' Men of the stature of Enrico Fermi and Arthur Compton would quiet down and listen."

Battelle fabricated the uranium fuel rods for the first full-scale reactor built at Oak Ridge. Lacking the proper equipment, they commandeered the plant of a little Ohio company that made aluminum stripping for kitchens. There, surrounded by armed guards, the uranium rods were extruded.

Zirconium in pure metallic form was also required for reactors, because it does not readily absorb neutrons. None was available, but a few years earlier some Battelle researchers had experimented

28

with making pure zirconium by decomposing vapors of zirconium chloride or iodide. With further development work, the process was commercialized and the Manhattan District was able to procure all the zirconium needed.

When nuclear reactors began functioning and made available radioactive isotopes, Battelle researchers were ready to use them for research. In fact, they had pioneered in the use of radioactive tracers as far back as 1937, when some prepared in The Ohio State University cyclotron were incorporated in metals to study the wear of piston rings.

The Jet that Couldn't Fly

Battelle men were called in when the prototype of the British Whittle jet engine was sent to the United States shortly after Pearl Harbor. Howard Cross, who attended the meeting, recalls with amusement that an Air Force colonel said: "Fellows, here's a real easy job. It has no reciprocating parts; just sucks in air and goes 'round and 'round." The first Whittle engine, however, was little more than a toy; it could not generate enough thrust to lift itself off the ground, much less propel an airplane, and the turbine blades lasted no more than a dozen hours.

To make jet airplanes fly, alloys were needed that would remain strong at a temperature of 1,500 degrees Fahrenheit and a pressure of 7,000 pounds per square inch. None were known at the time, but by the end of the war 100 had been tested (many at Battelle) and 10 were found adequate. Cross built most of the creep-testing equipment to measure an alloy's strength and staying power under such extreme conditions, and he himself carried out many of the evaluations.

Contract research for industry continued, although it was overshadowed by the numerous military projects. For instance, silver producers had come to Battelle before the war and signed a contract to develop new uses for their metal. Russ Dayton, assigned to the project, worked with manufacturers to develop better bearings for the radial engines that were built by the thousands for military aircraft. Steel bearings were smoother and longer-lasting if they were first electroplated with silver, then given a thin coating of a soft metal such as lead or indium.

Dayton was also the first Battelle man involved in a tiny project

29

with an independent inventor named Chester Carlson. Beginning on a small scale in 1944, a few researchers worked part-time to perfect a dry-copying process that Carlson had conceived. Though almost unnoticed in the midst of frantic wartime activity, this project turned out to be the most momentous that Battelle ever undertook. It resulted in xerography and, about a decade later, undreamed-of affluence for both Carlson and the Institute. The story is the subject of the next chapter.

End of Intimacy

The atmosphere at Battelle changed drastically during the war. People were required to wear badges and pass the scrutiny of security guards. For the first time they had to file detailed expense accounts and justify them with receipts. So many were hired that it was impossible to be on a first-name basis with everyone; sometimes men in adjacent offices or laboratories remained strangers for weeks. Some close friends seldom saw each other, for Battelle started working three shifts. Men without families often chose the night shift, not only to be accommodating, but also because they were then less likely to wait in line to use a particular machine or instrument. At least to this extent, the informal work-as-you-please rules of the early days were preserved.

Postwar Boom

An expected postwar slump never materialized at Battelle. Some government contracts phased out, but others were started. Industry looked to research as never before, for much wartime invention needed translation into the civilian economy.

Work on titanium, which was to become a Battelle mainstay for the next decade and more, began quite by accident late in 1946. Cross was touring the Royal Aircraft Establishment in Farnborough, England, when he was shown titanium being melted in a glass vacuum jar. Up to then, titanium, produced in fairly large amounts, had been a most unmetal-like metal: it was almost as brittle as glass. Upon inquiry, he learned that the British had been buying titanium pellets from a U.S. company. They tested each pellet by hitting it with a hammer. If it shattered, it was discarded, but if it simply flattened, it was added to the small stock of malleable titanium metal.

Cross returned excited, for titanium's basic properties—light weight combined with good performance at fairly high temperatures—were beginning to be needed for the kinds of jet aircraft then in the design stage. He got 50 pounds of titanium powder and then ordered 200 more under a Navy contract.

After helping to find ways to eliminate brittleness (which was caused by certain specific impurities), Battelle researchers, headed by Gonser and Robert Jaffee, compounded alloys, literally thousands of them, and tested their properties. They also developed techniques for rolling, forging, welding, and fabricating titanium alloys in other ways. Most of the work was sponsored under contracts with the U.S. Air Force and Remington Arms, but another industrial sponsor, Crucible Steel, got titanium patents that have been worth millions of dollars. The heyday of titanium research lasted until 1960; now after a decade of relative inactivity it is opening up again, because more military planes are flying faster and need titanium parts.

Meanwhile, research on more familiar metals continued to increase. Reminiscent of work in the 1930s on the selenium residue from copper-refining was a study of rhenium metal, which also occurs in copper ores. Rhenium had always been too brittle to be useful, but a group of researchers under Jaffee learned how to make it ductile. They found one use for rhenium in electrical contacts and another as an alloying ingredient that decreased the brittleness of the ultra-high-temperature metals: niobium, tantalum, molybdenum, and tungsten. Whereas rhenium had been a waste product, a rhenium shortage soon developed.

Fuel for Admiral Rickover

Battelle continued to pursue its wartime interest in atomic energy, and with great success. In 1949 the Institute developed prototypes of the fuel elements for the extremely compact nuclear reactor in the *Nautilus,* the first atomic submarine. In the same year chemists came up with an economical process that is still used to extract uranium from low-grade ores.

In 1954, the Institute bought 400 acres of land near West Jefferson, Ohio, 15 miles west of Columbus. There in semi-isolation it constructed a large-scale nuclear laboratory that includes "hot" cells with five-foot-thick concrete walls and windows for experiments with highly radioactive materials. It built also the first large nuclear reactor ever owned by a private organization. New and larger hot-cell facilities, scheduled for completion in 1972, will enable Battelle to evaluate fuels and other materials for most of the nuclear power industry.

Shortly after the war the Institute expanded its contacts with the oil and gas industry. The work included the improvement of drill rigs, conversion of the Big Inch and Little Inch oil pipelines to convey natural gas instead of liquid petroleum products, and detective work to discover why big fuel pipes sometimes rupture.

Research interests proliferated, but most projects were still mainly empirical studies of the physical and chemical properties of materials and their applications. As late as 1956 the staff included relatively few biologists and one professionally trained economist (although an Engineering Economics Division had been started in 1948).

At Grips with the Information Explosion

Battelle entered the "soft" sciences through a back door. In 1955, when the problems of titanium seemed to be overtaking the promise, the Defense Department contracted for the establishment of a Defense Metals Information Center (DMIC) at Columbus. Since the Institute had been slow to adopt computers, the center was not automated; the information was typed on large file cards and retrieved by picking them out of drawers. Nonetheless, it was a model of logical organization.

The information was (and still is) fed in by a nationwide network of some 3,000 contributors—all full-time working scientists who devote no more than 25 percent of their time to gathering and processing reports. Rather than submitting brief abstracts, they prepare thoroughly analyzed and interpretive extracts with key words underlined. These can be retrieved with the aid of a dictionary and thesaurus of technical words.

The system is not elegant or lightning fast, but it has proved more useful than computerized libraries containing information that has not been critically screened by experts in the subject matter. John Murdock, head of Battelle's information systems activities, says of DMIC: "We pride ourselves on being able to give a man the one article he most needs, not a paper blizzard of twenty or thirty articles more or less related to his inquiry." The DMIC contains 80,000 documents on aluminum, beryllium, titanium, the ultra-high-temperature metals, high-strength steels, superalloys, and ceramics. It is supplemented by mailings of published reports on research problems that need solving and by newsletters on timely topics.

DMIC has proved so useful that it has set a style for other information centers at Battelle. They include: the Copper Data Center; the U.S. headquarters for a worldwide center on cobalt and its uses; the Air Force's Battery Center; a biological and ecological index keyed to the possibility that a new Panama Canal will be constructed by nuclear blasting; a compendium on equipment and tools for deep-sea divers; and others concerning instruments and nondestructive testing.

Most of this vast store of information is being partly computerized, but sponsors do not seem to mind the scantiness of high-speed data-processing equipment. In 1971 the Dow Chemical Company transferred to Battelle all the 14,000 documents in its Metallurgical Research Laboratory as a data base for an International Magnesium Research Center operated by Battelle. Subsequently, Dow signed a $1,000,000 five-year contract for research at the new center.

A Crisis of Affluence

The early 1950s brought unprecedented prosperity to the Institute. Never before had contracts multiplied so rapidly; the two new European laboratories appeared to be holding their own; and the prospects of enormous income from the tiny venture in xerography began to materialize. But along with growth and prosperity came management problems. Battelle had become too large and complex to be run informally by a small group of close friends.

The first attempt at scientific management was launched in 1953 with the appointment of Lloyd Jackson, a veteran electrical engineer, to head a committee charged with coordinating plans. He and his associates drew up volumes, crammed with charts and tables, forecasting needs for staff, buildings, and equipment. The projections were carefully made but for the most part ignored.

The old concept of every able man being an entrepreneur running his own small income-producing center also began to cause confusion. Divisions had proliferated until there were some fifty of them, with all the chiefs reporting directly to Williams. Reorganization into seven departments helped to establish top management control. A little later, there was, however, a good deal of merriment when a metallurgy and a physics department were merged in another shuffle; for some time the new entity was referred to as the "Department of Metaphysics."

A good many men who were with Battelle at this time agree that the average quality of research slumped for two or three years, though not disastrously. A single Gillett could not have monitored such a busy institution, and attempts to form committees to do that quality-control job did not succeed. Yet Battelle continued to expand and prosper. Somehow within a few years it regained its equilibrium, even though a period of still more profound change was to follow.

CHAPTER FIVE

Xerography

The tens of thousands of applications filed with the U.S. Patent Office before 1900 bear witness to the dreams of a nation of tinkerers. Mostly these were lone visionaries—the Eli Whitneys, Samuel Colts, Elias Howes, Charles Goodyears, and even the Samuel Morses and Thomas Edisons—whose lives more often followed the tortured paths of frustration than of realization and riches. In the more complex world of the twentieth century, however, invention and technical innovation began to assume another pattern—that of the organized institutions that generally knew what they were looking for, took a highly sophisticated approach to invention, and set out systematically to solve their problems on the basis of a carefully justified investment of funds.

Battelle Memorial Institute has been from the start clearly such an institution, one almost wholly dedicated to the organized investigation of needed technologies or technological improvements. It was not likely to take on the unproved child of some lone inventor's inspiration and push it through from dream to workable process to marketable device. Yet this is just what Battelle did.

Possibly this was because the dream was well formulated and scientifically sound. More likely it was because Battelle, regardless of the formalities of its makeup, has always been more an aggregation of individuals than a structured organization.

The catalyst in this case was Russell Dayton, who had come to work for Battelle in 1934, after getting his doctorate in metallurgy. In connection with some research work for P. R. Mallory & Company, an Indianapolis maker of electronics and special battery equipment, Dayton had gone to New York to see Chester Carlson,

35

a Mallory patent attorney, early in 1944. Mallory had been turned down on its application for a patent based on Battelle's work, and Dayton was to testify on the matter the following day.

When their business was finished, Carlson asked, "Does Battelle ever take on the development of ideas for other people?"

"No," answered Dayton, "we never have."

"Would they consider it?" And Carlson produced a copy of a patent he had been granted for his own invention: an electrophotographic copying process.

Dayton read it over carefully. As he read, he grew more and more excited about what he saw. He took a copy of the patent back to Columbus with him. There he showed it to John Crout, who then headed the Battelle Development Corporation (BDC), a not-for-profit subsidiary. As Crout read the patent, it was his turn to grow excited. He asked Dayton to have Carlson come to Columbus for talks.

Chester Carlson's Invention

Chester Carlson was something of an anachronism: at a time when invention had become largely the province of highly trained people in well-equipped laboratories, he was still working out his ideas over the kitchen sink. Carlson, however, was not only a skilled patent attorney, but had earned a degree in physics from the California Institute of Technology.

Yet his had been a life of hard times and hard luck. He was born in Seattle in 1906 to parents of Swedish extraction; his mother was sickly, his father a migrant barber who suffered from arthritis. He began to help support his family when he was eleven, carrying newspapers and doing odd jobs day and night—washing windows, sweeping out offices, setting type for a newspaper. His father became bedridden when Chester was thirteen, and the boy became the sole breadwinner for the family, supporting both his parents until they died. Even so, he managed to scrape together enough money to enroll at Cal Tech, from which he graduated into the Depression in 1930.

He found work at the Bell Telephone Laboratories in New York City, where he started in research, was reassigned to liaison with the patent department, and was then laid off in 1933 as a Depression casualty. Carlson secured a job with the patent law firm of Austin and Dix, and at night attended the New York Law School. Warned that he might have to be laid off by the law firm, he found a position as a patent attorney for P. R. Mallory.

As a lawyer, he was very conscious of the tedious and time-consuming processes of copying contracts, pleadings, and briefs, and of sending out drawings to be photocopied. Deciding that there was a real need for a fast, inexpensive means of making copies, he set out to invent one.

In the New York Public Library, he started to search the literature on the many ways in which light affects matter. He knew that such established giants as Eastman Kodak were already exploring all the possibilities of silver-halide photography and chemical image transfers. But he felt that a dry process, if one could be found, would be more practical for office use. So his thinking turned toward photoelectrical means. Carlson found the writings of Paul Selyeni, who had shown that electrostatically charged particles could be attracted to a surface to form a predetermined pattern. "It was obvious to start experimenting with photoelectric and photoconductive materials," he later said. A photoelectric substance gives forth electrons under the influence of light, while a photoconductive one becomes a better conductor of electricity in light. It was known that sulfur, for example, would have its conductive properties increased by a factor of something like 1,000,000 when exposed to light.

Putting these ideas together gave Carlson his central idea: put an electrostatic charge on a film of photoconductive material; expose part of the surface of the material to light, so that part (and only that part) would lose its charge to some other material, leaving charged only the areas not struck by light; find some way to transfer the latent image of the electrically charged portion so that the image might become visible, and then transfer the developed image to a medium such as paper to serve as a permanent copy. On the basis of this idea, he filed his first patent application on October 18, 1937 for the process he called "electrophotography." Because his idea was completely innovative, he was able to get very broad patent protection.

Carlson went to work on further developments. When his wife objected to the fumes in their Long Island apartment, he rented a small apartment over a bar in Astoria. Not mechanically inclined himself, he hired an Austrian refugee, Otto Kornei, in the fall of

1938 to help him with his model. They coated a metal plate with sulfur, then rubbed it with a cotton handkerchief to give it an electrostatic charge. They then inked on a glass slide this legend:

10–22–38

Astoria

They placed the slide on the plate, and exposed the sulfur coating to a floodlamp for three seconds. The plate was then dusted with dyed lycopodium powder, a yellowish moss spore with relatively uniform spherical particles. The powder clung to the charged portion of the sulfur coating, and some of the lycopodium particles were then transferred to waxed paper pressed against the plate. The paper was then heated to melt the wax and fuse the powder image. This produced a very crude representation of the legend that had been inked onto the slide, but an image nonetheless.

Carlson then began making the rounds of companies—some twenty or more—that might wish to develop and market his invention. These demonstrated, he said, "an enthusiastic lack of interest," and were unable to see its commercial potential. Meanwhile, he continued to improve and embellish the process, and applied for more patents, including one for his hand-built copying machine.

So it was with slender hope of arousing interest that Carlson told Russ Dayton about his invention. But that encounter set into motion a long series of fateful and at times astounding events. In the end, Carlson was a rich man; Battelle had expanded far beyond anyone's dreams; and a small company became a corporate giant.

Battelle Goes to Work

At the meeting with Carlson in Columbus were Dayton, Crout, Howard Russell, Battelle's chief physicist, and Roland Schaffert, an engineer working on printing industry projects under Bruce Gonser. When Carlson gave a demonstration of his primitive process, Dayton remarked, "However crude this may seem, this is the first time any of you have seen a reproduction made without any chemical reaction and by a dry process."

They discussed possible applications, of which Carlson himself had a long list. Office copying was an obvious one, although no one for years afterward came close to guessing the potential of that market. Other suggested uses were for newspapers, catalogue-printing, printers for aircraft recorders, printouts for truck-scale readings, and toy kits. In a memorandum to Crout on April 5, 1944, Schaffert said: "When, and if, the development . . . reaches the point where a well-defined transferable . . . image can be obtained, consideration may be given to . . . such applications as duplicating to replace carbon copying, mimeographing, photocopying, lithographic or photo-offset printing . . . photoengraving and production of relief printing surfaces . . . and copy preparation and . . . the production of original text matter or photocomposition."

Schaffert's memo also focused on some of the problems, such as getting a sharp definition of the electrical image and finding a workable technique for transferring it to a printable medium. He suggested starting with an investigation of photoelectric and photoconductive materials, then finding some means of fixing the image on a "printable" surface. His conclusion: "This process looks like a good research gamble."

Crout agreed with the conclusion, even though he sensed that "the technical problems were enormous." The basic objective, he was aware, was to get a sufficient differential charge between exposed and unexposed areas and to maintain it long enough to put it through a process. Not too much was known at the time about photoconductivity or, for that matter, about triboelectricity, the process by which two substances take on opposite electrostatic charges when rubbed together, such as cotton against sulfur or cat's fur against glass. He nevertheless recommended that the Battelle Development Corporation put money into the project. Williams, who had been briefed by Russell and Schaffert, gave it the go-ahead, a decision that was approved by the Board.

The final agreement with Carlson was concluded in October, 1944. BDC would pursue research and development work, and Carlson named BDC as his agent to negotiate and grant licenses under his U.S. and Canadian patents. Carlson would receive 40 percent of all royalties, and BDC 60 percent, but Carlson was to get a guaranteed minimum royalty starting in 1948. After BDC invested $10,000 in research, it would receive an additional 1 percent of royalties, taken from Carlson's share, for each added $1,000 put into the project, up to $15,000, except that Carlson had the right to retain his full 40 percent share if he reimbursed BDC by

December 31, 1947, for half of BDC's expenditures over $10,000. BDC embarked on the project optimistically. Its annual report for 1944 said: "It is felt that this process has an excellent chance of succeeding in the majority of possible applications!"

Because both physics and chemistry were involved in the development, the work was assigned to both areas, with Schaffert in charge. Schaffert, who had been a printer and then a research physicist for Mergenthaler Linotype, first worked on the project with George Richards and Edward Wise. Then, as the war drew to a close, his Graphic Arts Division was expanded and others were assigned to the work, among them David Oughton, William Bixby, and Lewis Walkup.

At the start the investigators used plates of aluminum or brass, coated with sulfur or a coal-tar organic compound called anthracene. They rubbed the coating in the dark to give it an electrostatic charge, then laid film directly over the plate before exposing it to light. The results were anything but spectacular. Sulfur and anthracene were such poor photoconductors that long exposure times were required to drain the charge from the exposed areas, and a search went on for faster-acting coating materials.

Selenium was known to be a photoconductor, a fact that may have impressed itself on Battelle researchers a number of years before, when copper smelters and refiners had asked them to find new ways to use the quantities of selenium that piled up as a by-product. The trouble with selenium was that it was too good an electrical conductor in its grey metallic form, and would not hold a charge. Carlson had mixed sulfur and selenium (both of which are in the same family in the periodic table of elements), in order to combine the insulating properties of sulfur with the photochemical properties of selenium. He found, as expected, that the coating would not hold a charge when the mixture included a preponderance of selenium. At Battelle it was found that vacuum deposition (coating the plate by means of evaporating the substance in a vacuum) would produce a glasslike, or vitreous, form of selenium. In absolute darkness, this *did* hold a charge, although it would be discharged by the merest suggestion of light, even that of the "safe light" red lamp in a darkroom.

This turned out to be a development of major scientific significance. For a century, there had really been only one method of photography. This was the silver-halide process, by which one photon liberated an electron, and the electrons would accumulate on the site of an impurity to make an entire crystal chemically reducible to silver, in order to produce an image on film. The vitreous selenium also produced such a quantum multiplication of light; without that, electrophotography might have been no more than a competitor to the diazo process—and not a very good one, at that.

Battelle researchers also developed a way to pass wires carrying a high-voltage current over the plate, creating a corona and inducing an electrostatic charge on the plate. The corona discharge was also used to charge the paper to attract the powder from plate to paper. Battelle researchers worked out the triboelectric properties of various materials, and formulated a two-component developer to impart the proper electric charge to the particles used to bring out the latent electrostatic image on the coating of the plate.

These and other details, all developed at Battelle, made the new copying process infinitely more promising. Carlson was obviously impressed with the progress. When the time came for BDC to put more money into the development, he managed to borrow enough from relatives to put up his share, in order to retain his full equity in the royalties.

Enter Haloid

Battelle's success with electrophotography in the laboratory was not matched in its early efforts to find a manufacturer who would be willing to pay further development costs and to manufacture a device that would be marketable. But a prospective partner in the project did appear, quite by chance, at the psychologically right moment.

The Haloid Company had been formed in Rochester, New York in 1906 by a group of people who had split off from Eastman Kodak and by local investors who financed them. They went into the business of producing and marketing photographic paper, primarily for making photocopies. In the late 1920s, Haloid brought out a photoprinting paper of such superior quality that it virtually ran away with the market. But, gradually, competitors—chiefly Photostat Corporation, which had its paper sensitized by Eastman, and a small Rochester company called Rectigraph—caught up to Haloid. The competing firms, moreover, also made photostatic

41

copying machines, giving them a wide edge with the substantial number of customers who preferred to buy their paper from the makers of the equipment they used. By the late 1930s, recalled the late Joseph Wilson, at the time a vice-president, Haloid realized that "our position would be very difficult."

During the war Haloid was busy enough, but its market began to shrink as the war drew to a close. In 1935, Haloid acquired the competing Rectigraph Company and, along with it, a German-born chemist named John Dessauer. He became a research chemist for Haloid in the photography area, specializing in quality control. One of his assignments was to find new products that had better chances of avoiding head-on competition with the giants, Kodak and Ansco.

It was Dessauer who read, in the April, 1945, issue of the *Monthly Abstract Bulletin,* a publication put out by Eastman for its own scientific personnel and circulated to some outsiders, about an article describing an "electronic process of photography." Dessauer got the original article, written by Nicholas Langer for the July, 1944 issue of *Radio-Electronic Engineering,* and read it. Impressed, he suggested to Joseph Wilson that they explore this new process.

Wilson approached the matter gingerly. First he got two go-betweens—George Cameron and Ernest Taubes, whose own little firm, Microtonics, was then examining a photostatic camera for Haloid—to visit Carlson. They came away from the interview with enthusiasm for the process, and even said that the idea might be worth as much as $500,000. In December, 1945, Wilson and Dessauer went to Columbus for exploratory talks with Crout, Schaffer, Ed Graves, and Williams. Several months later, they were back to ask whether Battelle would be willing to give them a license for the new copying process.

Agreement was reached on these general terms: Haloid would be given a license for a machine that could make up to twenty copies in line copy form, their rights covering the United States and its territories and possessions. In return, Haloid was to sponsor further research on the project at Battelle for up to $25,000 a year, and to pay an 8 percent royalty on revenues from the process. The agreement was drafted and redrafted over a period of months. It was finally signed in December, 1946, to take effect on January 1, 1947.

For Haloid, it was an expensive gamble. The company's total earnings in 1946 had been only $101,000, on sales of $6.75 million. And Battelle might have had some serious misgivings as well. Haloid had just been through a management battle, from which Wilson's father (then president) had emerged the victor. Joseph Wilson, who was then named executive vice-president, recalled: "I've often wondered why Battelle allowed us to do it, in retrospect, because on paper we were not very good prospects for carrying it through. Financially, we were very limited, we had a limited marketing organization, limited research group. I guess what sold them was that we were going to make or break with it—either we were going to go under or we were going to do it. And they were afraid that bigger companies would have it as a side issue, on the back burner. So they allowed us to take this ball."

The Haloid people, familiar with the photocopying business, thought first of the copying field, but they considered other applications such as photoprinting, an instant camera, and enlarging from microfilm. Like the others, Haloid at the time had no real sense of the potential size of the office copying market. But they started to set up their own laboratory to engineer the required equipment and to build models of copiers, as well as to conduct chemical research and to help direct and verify the results of Battelle's work on the process.

There was general agreement that "electrophotography" would be a cumbersome and unimaginative name for a commercial product; so Robert Stith, in charge of Battelle public relations activities, undertook to find something catchier. He consulted a professor of classical languages at Ohio State University, who provided a number of choices. The one selected was *xerography,* from the Greek *xeros,* "dry," and *graphos,* "writing."

The first public disclosure of the new process, except for the Langer article of some years before, was at a Detroit meeting of the American Optical Society on October 22, 1948, ten years to the day after Carlson made his first successful image in Astoria. Haloid and Battelle joined in a demonstration at the meeting, and a paper was written for the Society's journal. Members of the Society were interested, but not overwhelmed. Most could not see how this new process differed greatly from other copying methods then available—photocopies, Apeco's photodiffusion, Diazo, and photo blueprinting. The most important outgrowth of this meeting may well have been the cementing of continued close cooperation between Haloid and Battelle.

New Negotiations and New Products

Not long after the first contract was negotiated with Haloid, it became obvious to both parties that the agreement was seriously flawed. It was quite clear that a printer for fewer than twenty copies could just as easily be used for more than twenty copies. An invention for printing on paper could also be used for printing on cloth, paperboard, or other materials. And Haloid, which had exceded its contractual $25,000 in annual sponsorship at Battelle, was concerned with a provision calling for any of its own developments to be incorporated into Battelle's patent position.

By mutual consent, the contract was renegotiated in May, 1948. Wilson retained Sol Linowitz, a brilliant young lawyer with the firm of Sutherland, Sutherland, Linowitz and Williams, to conduct the new negotiations. Linowitz performed so well for Haloid that he later became chairman of the company's board of directors. Under the new arrangement, Haloid was made the exclusive licensee, worldwide (except for a few applications such as toys), and the requirement for Haloid sponsorship of Battelle research was eliminated. But the royalty remained at 8 percent.

Largely to protect its own interests, Haloid gradually took over much of the research, although Battelle was still called on for some work. With some help from Batelle, equipment engineering was begun very early. The first device was simply a wooden box enclosing the elements that had been developed at Battelle. It was called the XeroX copier (Wilson admitted the influence of "Kodak" in the choice of a name for the product); about a dozen were built. As a copying device the equipment was almost a total failure. It was slow, dirty to use, awkward to operate, and required about fourteen different manual operations. They included charging the plate, covering it with a dark slide, placing the plate in the exposure device, removing the slide, making the exposure, covering with the slide, putting the plate over the developer tray, removing the slide, developing the image, transferring it to paper, cleaning up the plate, peeling off the paper, fusing the image onto the paper, and hoping for a picture. A good picture would result if all the steps were done slowly and carefully; otherwise it was difficult to judge what had gone wrong.

Haloid might have lost heart at this time, but serendipity stepped in. The Addressograph-Multigraph Corporation was then marketing an offset office printing press, one of whose drawbacks was the time and expense involved in making paper offset master plates. Copies made on paper lithographic plates in Haloid's wooden box turned out to be completely suitable for the purpose.

The first commercial installation of the XeroX machine came late in 1950. Addressograph helped sell it to its own customers, and for a number of years Haloid made a respectable profit from an application that had not been foreseen when the machine was first built. This model went through a number of changes and variations, the final one of which, perfected in 1953, was called the Lithmaster. Its major contribution was to provide some profits and much of the experience that Haloid needed to create an automatic office copier—the central objective on which Wilson had settled.

Developing the copier proved a great strain on Haloid's resources. The company earned a total of $2.3 million from its established business from 1947 to 1952, but this was needed for normal growth. To develop xerography, Haloid had to go outside to raise $4.3 million.

The next development was the Copyflo, which grew out of a machine made for the Air Force to produce enlarged prints from microfilm. The Air Force machine performed all the steps automatically, but sequentially, and the product was printed on separate sheets. The later commercial application was significantly speeded up by performing all the steps automatically and simultaneously, and it printed on a paper roll from which sheets could be cut.

By the mid-1950s the Haloid machines were much improved, and sales and earnings had increased to the point where the company could afford to put some real money into the development of an automatic copying machine. Sales of $21 million in 1955 were three times as high as they had been in 1947, so that Battelle's 8 percent royalty became the source of substantial income. By the same token, however, the royalty payments were turning out to be a cash drain on Haloid that was a major barrier to rapid development of the office copier.

This half-pleasant, half-nettlesome dilemma affected both parties.

It was now clear that there would be a substantial continuing income from the machines. Battelle, which had taken the early risks and contributed so much of substance to the state of the art, was naturally desirous of participating in future profits. As for Haloid, the company was aware that the Carlson patents were coming close to expiration, and that its own commercial advantage would then depend on improvements and developments already made and still to come.

The idea of solving the problem by turning Battelle's interest into an equity position in Haloid may have occurred to a number of different people on both sides, but it was probably Linowitz who first voiced the suggestion that Battelle give up the 8 percent cash royalty in return "for some paper." So negotiations were reopened, and carried on over a period of several months.

The new agreement, reached late in 1955, provided that Haloid would give Battelle 50,000 shares of its stock in exchange for an assignment of the basic Carlson patents, and another 5,000 shares for the other patents and patent applications related to the project. Royalty payments were reduced in a subsequent agreement to 3 percent on the first $20 million in domestic sales and 1 percent on all sales above that figure, for the years 1959 to 1965 inclusive. Battelle had the right to request half the royalty payment in stock, at the rate of $60 per share (slightly higher than the market value at the time), but Haloid could limit the number of shares to 5,000 in any one year. It was also agreed that Battelle would assign any inventions in the field to Haloid, as long as Haloid maintained a xerography research program of at least $25,000 a year, exclusive of government research.

Like all the other agreements between Battelle and Xerox, this one was negotiated with sensitivity and amicability. While all the basic contracts between these two parties were necessarily reduced to written form, they were bulwarked by unwritten understandings between the contracting parties. Long afterward, Wilson would still speak with warmth of his relationships with Crout, Graves, Schaffert, Williams, Walkup, and others. And Crout tells of a tacit understanding that all agreements be advantageous to both parties; he recalls that Wilson once said, in some puzzlement, about an agreement that had been reached, "That sounds fine, but I can't see what you're going to get out of it." Throughout the association, although Xerox must at times have been hard pressed for the kind of technical personnel it needed, it never pirated one individual from Battelle's staff—a procedure that many another Battelle sponsor thought of as almost part of the bargain.

Unexpected Riches

By 1959, Haloid was ready to manufacture and market its new office copier—the 914, so named because it could reproduce on paper that measured up to 9 inches by 14 inches. Because Haloid still needed cash, it offered to license the manufacture and sale of the machine to one of the nation's major corporations—the third time this corporation had been given an opportunity to enter the field. The company surveyed the market prospects, decided they were not good, and turned the offer down. At this point Wilson, who had gradually been building a strong marketing organization, decided that Haloid itself would make the machines and market them on a lease basis.

In the spring of 1960, after spending thirteen years and investing $40 million in the development of an office copier, Haloid brought out the 914. A desk-sized, fully automatic machine, it could produce the first copy in thirty seconds, additional copies at the rate of one every eight seconds. It could copy from black or colored inks, from single sheets, or from pages in a book. What Dessauer later described as taking an "enormous risk" was the decision "to have a readable copy every time, rather than the best possible copy after two or three tries."

All the decisions appear to have been right, because the 914 was an immediate success. Actual leasing in 1960 was about double what Haloid had expected. "Xerox®" quickly entered the language as a noun and adjective, and "to xerox" became a verb. (The trade name XeroX had long before been downgraded by common consent of users to Xerox®; the company had changed its name to Haloid Xerox in 1958, and it made a second change to Xerox Corporation in 1961.)

Because the law permitted the company to capitalize the cost of the patents, Xerox was able to get a good cash flow for the purposes of sales development and financing leased machines, at a time when this was critically important. Leasing gave the company another advantage, since it was able to amortize capital costs over short periods. Once the machines were fully depreciated, rental income kept flowing in, so that further development was facilitated. In 1962, the company's gross revenues reached $100 million. By 1965, the 914 copier accounted for some 62 percent of total operating revenues, or almost a quarter of a billion dollars.

In 1963 the company brought out its first desk-top copier, the 813. It did not catch on immediately. Perhaps it was because the 914 had become a waiting-line proposition, with customers clamoring for it, so that they felt the 813 was for second-class corporate citizens. Or perhaps so much effort had gone into overcoming resistance to the idea of the large desk-sized machine that potential buyers now felt the smaller model would be inadequate. But in time the 813 also took off and became a money-maker.

Another large model, the Xerox 2400 copier-duplicator, was brought to the market in 1965. Named for its ability to produce 2,400 copies per hour—40 per minute—at the touch of a button, this model was responsible for most of the company's growth by 1967. The company's own investments in research and engineering rose from $1,000,000 in 1956 to more than $48 million in 1967.

By 1969 Xerox Corporation had unmistakably joined the giants; its worldwide revenues had reached $1.48 billion, more than 200 times as great as they had been in the year before the original agreement with Battelle took effect. Its stock, increased about 1,200 times in value in the same period, was worth about $8 billion.

Under the 1955 agreement, stock that eventually was worth $500 million was turned over to Battelle and Carlson. His long years of privation and struggle ended, Carlson used much of his money to help others. Arthritis-ridden in his later years, he spent long hours evaluating numerous requests for money from others. He helped youngsters through college and donated a building to Cal Tech. When he died of a heart attack at the age of 62 in 1968, most of his estate was left to colleges and social agencies.

Battelle's share of the funds, amounting to almost 100 times its original $3.5 million endowment, enabled the research institute to reach out to new horizons in "the discovery of new and advanced metallurgical or other processes and the better education of men," as Gordon Battelle's will had stipulated.

Battelle has continued to do work sponsored by Xerox Corporation and has made major contributions to the progress of the copying art. In all, Battelle researchers were responsible for 164 patents granted in the field of xerography from 1947 to 1970. Beyond that, the Xerox experience served to document the value of dreams. Many a Battelle researcher, on the trail of some exciting discovery or intriguing hunch, has been spurred to better efforts by the thought that he might be en route to "the next Xerox."

CHAPTER SIX

The Venture Divisions

"Inherently I always believe in making money out of ideas," Clyde Williams has said. And Battelle's ideas, he knew, would either be sold to industry or they would languish. Its people, with their great technological capability and creative potential, were "boiling over" with new ideas which industry saw no reason to support. Williams felt that an appropriate vehicle for developing some of the more marketable ideas generated at Battelle could be a source of income; the Board went along with his notion. So in 1935, still in his first year as director of the Institute, he formed Battelle Development Corporation as a not-for-profit corporation.

BDC's purpose was to run with the ball when nobody else would, and when there was a chance it might be carried across the goal line—or at least for good yardage. It was designed to work on ideas that were patentable, but not immediately salable. "We take ideas nobody else wants to sponsor," BDC General Manager John Gray has said, "and carry them through their high-risk period to the point where industry will take them over."

In the early days, BDC's work tended to be colored by the special interests of the men who were put in charge. The first was John Sullivan, who simultaneously directed the Ceramics and Process Metallurgy Divisions. Given a small appropriation, he ran the new development arm on a shoestring, concentrating on a number of small projects, mainly in his own specialties. A top technical man, Sullivan turned out to be much better at supervising BDC research than licensing its patent rights to outside companies.

In 1941, at Sullivan's urging, David Minton came to work for Battelle, hardly endearing himself to his bosses when he announced that he would give the Institute a whirl for a year or two. Minton had taken degrees at the University of Arizona at the time that Sullivan was chief metallurgist for the Arizona station of the U.S. Bureau of Mines, located at the University, and Minton had since taught at Arizona and at the University of the Philippines. Sullivan soon had Minton helping him in BDC, where Minton looked over the portfolio of patents and announced that it was all but worthless—and that more money was going into the patents than BDC was getting out of them. Time, however, did not permit Minton to do anything to reverse this situation. He soon went to Washington, at Williams' urging, as administrative officer of the War Metallurgy Committee.

Another strong business sense was brought into BDC when John Crout became general manager in 1942. By this time the development corporation's budget had grown to an almost respectable $50,000 to $75,000 a year. One of the earliest BDC projects—and also one of the handful that have ever generated income—was the electropolishing of stainless steel, and this was providing royalty income at the time. Battelle had first gone into electroplating, and then electropolishing, an electrolytic treatment in which material is removed from the surface of the anode in such a way that high points are progressively attacked, giving the surface an even more highly polished effect than can be obtained from wheel polishing or buffing. BDC had licensed various electroplating shops, as well as those working on stainless steel automobile bumpers, to use this process.

But BDC's great coup under Crout's leadership, of course, was the decision to devote a substantial part of its budget to fund electrophotography—a decision that was to change radically the scope of BDC's operations, and that of Battelle Memorial Institute's even more. "It was a perfect thing for BDC to finance," says Crout, "just because there were a lot of problems to be solved. There were basic problems of physics and chemistry, and problems of mechanical engineering in developing a machine." It was also a basic invention, with a variety of possible markets that might be developed.

After the war, Ed Graves took over as BDC manager, and he was succeeded after several years by Russ Deubner, both of them under Crout's general supervision. Deubner remained in the post until 1958, during which period BDC licensed a number of patented items, including a process for waterproofing leather and a typewriter correction fluid marketed under the trade name of Snopake®. Toward the end of this period, BDC's royalty income amounted to about $350,000 a year, most of it from xerography. Says Deubner: "If there hadn't been an entity like BDC, xerography would not have come through Battelle at all."

When Deubner was moved into the Economics Division, where he did new product work and diversification studies for companies, Crout moved back into direct charge of BDC. He was succeeded by John Gray, who had become a patent attorney for BDC in 1949 and its general counsel a few years later. Gray retained his legal responsibilities after he became assistant general manager of BDC in 1960 and vice-president and general manager when Crout retired in 1964.

How BDC Works

In the early days, all the projects that BDC sought to develop got their initial impetus from within Battelle Memorial Institute, and BDC invariably got its economic and technical services from the Institute. In time, BDC began to entertain ideas from outside sources (with xerography as the outstanding example), sometimes through the purchase of patents. But BDC's chief interest remained in inventions in their embryonic stages, which might come from any of the four Battelle laboratories, from individuals, from universities (BDC has agreements with fifty leading universities), or from industry itself, particularly when a company has an invention that does not fit its own manufacturing or marketing interests.

Each year BDC looks at about 1,000 inventions, in various stages of development, and selects about 25 for funding. The criteria for this selection include patentability, technical feasibility, and the nature, size, and penetrability of markets. In the development phase of its work, BDC seeks to establish a patent position, to seek market information, and to undertake research and development programs that will minimize the ultimate manufacturer's risks. In the world in which BDC operates, the progression from conception of an idea to its entry into the marketplace requires a minimum of ten years—and more likely fifteen, or even twenty-five. Not more than three or four of the 1,000 examined annually will ever reach the market, and not all of these will be successful. Each idea or innovation may involve a plurality of products, and its development costs to BDC will run anywhere from $35,000 to $800,000. In the company's entire history, not more than about a dozen developments have eventually paid their own way.

BDC operates with approximately twenty professionals, three of them patent lawyers, a half dozen in the business operation, and the rest, spread around the four Battelle laboratories, with backgrounds in technical fields or in research and development management. When a project appears to be ready for commercial application, the next phase is licensing its use or manufacture. Licensing is tailored to each development, and a separate plan is worked and implemented for each. If this involves starting a new enterprise, BDC does not engage in its management functions, although the development corporation usually takes a minority interest—which may be as high as 49 percent, but still a minority. After a development is licensed, there is often more work to be done in reinforcing the patent position, undertaking further development, and liaison with the licensee. The licensees of BDC patents spend as much or more in further research at the four laboratories as BDC itself.

There are differences, perhaps inevitable, that spring up between BDC and researchers at the laboratories. Research engineers are sometimes annoyed at BDC's reluctance to support a laboratory's own pet developments, while BDC, a hardheaded client seeking to minimize costs, resists what it considers excess research on a project. Unlike an in-house research project, whose ultimate product will often be a well-thought-out and scholarly paper, BDC's objective is something that industry will be willing to take on.

In earlier times, BDC tended to "harvest wild ideas," according to President Sherwood Fawcett, but now it is much more in the business of harvesting systematic ideas—looking at an area that is ripe for ideas, picking out the most urgent needs, and trying to find a way to meet them. BDC long felt slighted in the amounts budgeted for its operations, and its employees felt that the growth possibilities were limited. In 1964, the budget was increased sharply, to around $2 million. As for BDC's continuing insistence that it was responsible for the great xerography cornucopia, Fawcett says, only half in jest, that it is impossible to tell with what frequency BDC can score such major successes until it comes up with another Xerox.

The For-Profit Company

If BDC introduced a new dimension to Battelle operations, in time it also pointed up another major shortcoming in the march of ideas to the marketplace—the unwillingness of private industry to accept some new developments, simply because they were not big enough or because they did not show enough immediate promise to undertake the expense of commercial marketing. So, late in 1962 Battelle moved into this vacuum, too, organizing Scientific Advances, Inc. (SAI) on a risk-for-profit basis.

SAI started operations a few months later, with the objective of taking high-risk products, building them up, forming new companies to market them, then going public or disposing of the companies once they were making money. In the beginning SAI concentrated on new product lines, rather than companies, with the provision that they involve a high degree of technology. Among the earliest products were the Diatype® typing teacher aid, a SE-LIN® labeler line for encoding library books, and a subminiature pressure transducer now sold under the Sensotec® mark. This last, invented by Nelson Crites in the Engineering Systems Department at Battelle-Columbus, has a diaphragm surface and strain-gauge sensors which detect and measure fluid pressure; these were attached to helicopter blades, for one application, to find the pressure of airflow around the blade; they can also be used medically as probes to measure pressure changes in the esophagus.

SAI is not interested in competing with established business firms, but tends to go where normal risk capital is not available, and to stay with a situation only until such capital becomes available. It does, however, seek out fields that have the potential of building a viable business. SAI will normally do a technical and an economic feasibility study, either by itself or on subcontract to a Battelle laboratory or some other outside resource. It also

55

evaluates patents, improves or enhances the strength of existing patents, obtains financial and tax advice, and performs management consulting and market studies. While its policy is one of taking a majority interest in any company it organizes, it seeks to dispose of such companies when they are prepared to operate on a profitable basis.

SAI now has a majority interest in about ten different companies. It has not yet completed a full cycle of exploring a potential product, developing it, strengthening the patent position, starting a company, marketing the product, and disposing of the company, but some are ready or soon will be ready for the final step. One such company is NORTEC, which grew out of some of the Pacific Northwest Laboratories' developments in nondestructive testing. Their first instrument was a unit that could detect defects in tubing in place in a heat exchanger. This inspection capability is of great importance in nuclear power plants. This work then expanded into other uses of ultrasonic and eddy-current techniques. SAI owns virtually all of NORTEC, which is now profitable, cash-generating, and ready for disposition.

NORTEC, incidentally, introduced SAI to Unirad, a struggling little Denver company that purchased NORTEC transducers to use in its own field of ultrasonic medical diagnostics. SAI acquired Unirad, which now has additional products and, in its second year of sales, is verging on profitability. Most recently, it has done a metabolic screening capable of determining fetal deformities.

In 1969 it was felt that SAI's relationship with Battelle might conceivably compromise the tax-exempt position of the parent organization, and the management of SAI was separated out entirely, with a board that has a majority of outside members. At the same time SAI's mission was redefined to place greater emphasis on starting industries aimed at the economic development of regions or areas—with the projects scaled, of course, to SAI's capabilities and limited resources.

For some projects, the logical research-development-marketing chain has been followed from the Battelle laboratories to BDC to SAI. One of these was Electrospin, a method for the electrostatic spinning of yarn, which emanated from the Geneva laboratory, where it was invented by Maurice Poull and André Corbaz. It was patented there and, with BDC funding, was brought to the point where its feasibility was demonstrated. Unlike traditional methods of yarn-spinning, which are "closed end" because of physical limitations in the speed of the spindles, electrostatic spinning is "open end" because there are theoretically no limitations on speed or fiber length. The fibers being spun float in thin air, being supported and guided by an electrostatic field. It has already been demonstrated at an international textile show in Paris with experimental equipment, operating at a speed several times that of traditional methods. When outside risk capital could not be found to undertake the entire project, SAI took it on jointly with North American Rockwell's Draper Division, in an arrangement whereby SAI had an initial 51 percent interest in Electrospin Corporation, but one that would later give the two partners equal ownership.

Just as SAI works as a potential licensee of BDC patents, it works with outsiders, not to do initial research, but to move a product along, usually at or near the market development stage. Because one of its roles is to judge the ultimate viability of ventures, it tends to put professional administrators rather than engineers on its staff.

Following the pioneering of 1971 Nobel Laureate Dennis Gabor in holography, researchers at the University of Michigan made some new discoveries in coherent radiation imaging, a way of using laser light to make three-dimensional pictures called holographs. BDC provided the development funds for this work in 1965. The result was a series of inventions, on which further research was done at the University and at two Battelle laboratories. SAI then picked up the project and formed a fifty-fifty joint venture with Dupont, called Holotron, to seek out commercial uses for this "off-axis" holography, e.g., three-dimensional photographs, information storage, and measurements of infinitesimal vibrations. Because the exploitation of holography appeared to require greater capability than SAI possessed, the marketing company decided to license its patents to others who appeared to have more elements of the needed capability package, while retaining its option to reactivate the initial project.

In combination, BDC and SAI have demonstrated additional avenues by which society can benefit from the achievements of scientific and technological research and discovery. Part of the fallout has undoubtedly been to encourage a great increase in venture divisions of large corporations, as an effort to create in the environment of such companies the conditions that will make for growth far in the future.

CHAPTER SEVEN

Battelle Abroad

As far back as World War I, Horace Gillett had been conscious of research progress abroad, and particularly of the metallurgical advances being made in Germany. Indeed, when Clyde Williams first went to work for Gillett at the U.S. Bureau of Mines in 1916, one of his earliest projects involved the development of high-alloy metal linings for the big guns, so that they could compete with Germany's Big Berthas. But it took World War II to arouse the kind of international consciousness that led Battelle Memorial Institute to think seriously of extending its laboratory operation abroad.

On a 1949 trip to Europe, Bert Thomas was deeply impressed with the need for research in European industry. In 1950, Williams instigated a survey of research in Europe, particularly in Germany, and it was found that contract research did not exist there. Some industries put money into German universities, but the professors used it to do what they wanted to do, which was not always what industry would like to have done. Germany's economy was still extremely depressed, and the study indicated that good industrial research might help stimulate industrial regrowth.

The postwar impediments to currency movements provided another stimulus to expansion abroad. Williams was friendly with Robert Bull, who headed the Electric Furnace Association, an organization for which Battelle had done work in the 1930s and early 1940s. Bull's son, Benton, a vice-president of Johnson & Johnson, called Williams one day to say that his company had a

59

lot of dollars tied up in Europe, and he asked whether they might use it to buy research—which of course *could* cross national borders, even though the money could not. The answer had to be no, since no contract research was then being done in Europe, but Battelle was spurred to examine the prospects more closely.

The first thoughts centered on a small laboratory in Geneva, both because of the international flavor of Switzerland and because the Swiss franc was convertible. In May, 1951, John Crout and Robert Keagy made an exploratory trip to Europe, visited Great Britain, the Netherlands (where they were joined in their tour by Frank Croxton, then attending the Third World Petroleum Conference there), France, Germany, Switzerland, and Italy. They decided early that the notion of using blocked currencies for research was not feasible, since it would require a separate laboratory in each country. But it could work for a single country, and the plan for a European laboratory met most enthusiastic response in Germany, where it was felt that an industrial research facility would act as an adjunct to the Marshall Plan in helping industry back on its feet.

At one point Crout was talking about manpower to Nobel Prize-winner Otto Hahn, who said, "We need these young scientists very badly if we're going to recover." Hahn then took from a shelf a three-inch-thick book listing the nation's scientists for 1930. Then he placed alongside it a similar one-inch volume that had just come off the press, and said, "You know, so many of them were Jewish . . . . We did treat these people very badly."

Crout and Keagy recommended the establishment of two European laboratories—one in Geneva, as an international center, and the other in Germany. The recommendation was approved by the Battelle Board, and the two men returned to Europe in September. They retained legal counsel, rented some space in former American consulate offices in downtown Geneva, and asked for Robert Adams to come over to get the German operation started. Adams arrived in October, and Williams and Thomas also went to Europe that fall, when Thomas set up an accounting system.

Starting the Frankfurt Laboratory

Max Barnick had done fundamental research at the Kaiser-Wilhelm-Institut (later the Max-Planck-Institut), and was with a new technical organization in Dusseldorf when Battelle was making its initial market study in Germany. Barnick's organization did its research wherever equipment might be available, channeling projects to existing facilities, and he thought of the proposed Battelle laboratory as another resource that might be used. When the Battelle people showed an interest in the Ruhr area, he was assigned to be their guide.

Crout, Thomas, and Adams were impressed enough with Barnick to offer him a job in March, 1952 as technical director of their new facility, and he accepted. The first order of business was to decide on a site, preferably one in an area with varied industry, good cultural facilities nearby, and a good technical university. A number of bürgermeisters were interviewed, and attractive offers were made by Stuttgart, Frankfurt, and Essen. Frankfurt, which offered a free site within the city limits and near the university, was selected. With an orchestra, a theater, and mixed industry, Frankfurt in many ways resembled Columbus.

Barnick started the wheels rolling on the registration as a non-profit association, which was obtained by mid-year. Space was rented in Dechema Haus, headquarters of the German association of chemical-plant equipment manufacturers, where something of a coup was scored by getting a room with a telephone already installed—almost the only way to have a phone at that time. In July, Gerald Keinath came to help with administrative problems, and Bill Welcker arrived to work on design and construction.

When plans had advanced far enough to start construction by the end of October, a group of German businessmen who might be interested in research were invited for cognac and cookies, a talk on contract research, and then dinner at a restaurant. About the same time five supervisors—in physics, chemistry, engineering, ceramics, and metallurgy—were hired and shipped off to Columbus for indoctrination in carrying on contract research.

An architectural competition was held in Germany for the new building. The most useful laboratory design, making provision for such characteristics as maximum flexibility, movable walls and partitions, heavy load capacity, and availability of electric power, had already been established through experience in the United States. Welcker had made five trips to Frankfurt, each lasting a month or more, by the summer of 1953, at which time the three buildings being erected were well along toward completion. At the dedication ceremonies in June, Clyde Williams delivered an address in passable German, and an open house—"the day of the open doors"—was held for visitors on a Sunday.

The last visitor of the day was an industrialist, to whom Barnick proceeded to sell a research contract in applied physics—a project that continued for several years. Among the earliest jobs in Germany was one in ceramics, and some foundry work followed. It soon became evident that the growth industries of the period—physics, electronics, chemistry—constituted a major market for contract research.

It turned out to be an ideal time for the start of the German laboratory. The German industrial revival was just getting rolling, and many firms needed all the help they could get. Moreover, there were dozens of applicants for every job. Says Frankfurt's Albert Schwarz, "I could pick you a chemist who was unmarried and came from Bavaria—or any other specifications you could name." The better universities might have offered stiff competition, but academic people were still insistent on doing the work they liked, or holding off a project until just the right graduate student came along, and on publishing their results immediately. Battelle suited industry much better on all counts, and in some cases industry turned to Frankfurt out of sheer frustration.

But Battelle-Frankfurt had its problems at the start. The concept of a not-for-profit organization was virtually unknown in Europe, and people there wondered what the angle was. There were also rivalries among the European nations, and a considerable residue of Germanophobia left from the war. During the Occupation, German companies were obliged to inform the Allies of any research they were doing. When this requirement was dropped, Battelle was variously accused of (1) being the new tool of the U.S. State Department, (2) spying for U.S. industry, (3) using Frankfurt to get research done at cut rates, and (4) recruiting scientists to be spirited off to America.

As a matter of fact, the brain drain to the United States was just starting, but this would have taken place with or without Battelle's presence. Battelle decided to use European nationals as directors and staff members, and not to undertake any European recruitment for Columbus. Projects were placed in Columbus or Europe on the basis of where they could be executed best, and the work was not actually done any less expensively in Frankfurt. As a matter of practice, most projects carried on there were for European industry—as much for non-German industry as for German, with a considerable amount of work coming from Great Britain.

Eventually, however, German industry got to know Battelle for what it was. Although the assumption had been that it would help primarily small and medium-sized companies, it turned out that the larger firms had a fuller appreciation of the value of research and could afford to take the calculated risks involved. By the end of 1953, the Frankfurt staff had grown to about seventy-five. Riding the crest of German revival, Frankfurt became self-supporting in only five years.

Geneva Beginnings

With Adams in Frankfurt, Keagy remained in charge in Geneva, where he helped do some of the initial staffing. One of the first people he hired—actually the seventeenth—was Hugo Thiemann, who had come to Geneva late in 1952 with the idea of starting an institute for applied physics at the University of Geneva. He had heard, both in Zurich and Geneva, of the plans for a new Battelle laboratory, and the Battelle people had also heard of Thiemann. He saw Keagy, who recruited him to build up a research activity in physics.

The Geneva operation was then being conducted in rented space in the very center of town. When an old château was located on the Sphelinger estate at the edge of town (Carouge), and remodeled, it became Battelle's new home in Geneva. An old barn was adapted as a shop, a storehouse, and for general utility purposes; in time, a new building was constructed.

Thiemann's first assignment was simply to think about the concept of such an institution as Battelle in Geneva. He began with the premises on which the Americans planned to operate: they had come to do in Europe precisely what they had been doing in America—acting as a problem-solver for industry. Thiemann decided that that approach was unrealistic for much of Europe, where there were not enough potential clients who could either define or finance research on problems. Battelle was not having much luck with this approach, as people in its offices in Paris, Milan, Madrid, and London tried to find sponsors who had problems to be solved. He decided that the Swiss research institute needed to define itself and its capabilities, and to conduct research and present it to potential sponsors as a *fait accompli,* or at least an idea well along in the process of being developed. This became and remained the guideline for the Geneva laboratory, where, Thiemann points out, most of what is done "is based on our own initiative." On this basis, he found Battelle became more attractive to topnotch European researchers.

Thiemann was soon given the job of building up a group of people with the kind of creative imagination he felt was required, which then enabled the laboratory to add projects. His major role soon took on an administrative character, at least informally, and he officially took on the title of general manager at the end of

1954. In that role, he retained his involvement in the formulation of problems, particularly when this meant the evolution of new lines of scientific endeavor with long-range implications for the laboratory.

At first it was planned that the Frankfurt Laboratories would cover Germany, while Geneva would take on the rest of Europe. The division did not quite work out that way, as Frankfurt began to get projects from other countries. Eventually Geneva tended to get business from the "Roman" countries and Frankfurt from the Germanic, with Britain and Spain going either way. But another division developed, based on the character of the laboratories and the nature of the project, with Geneva getting the basic research and Frankfurt the applied. This difference perhaps reflected more the character of the directors than the national settings. Another difference between the laboratories, as expressed by Schwarz, was that, especially at the beginning, "Germany needed Battelle; Switzerland tolerated it."

Building the European Operation

All or part of the administrative responsibilities in the European laboratories were taken over by Americans—Keagy, Adams, Keinath, Croxton—until the mid-1950s, when the European directors added these to their duties of technical supervision. As Frankfurt grew, it added divisions, then sometimes converted them to departments. In 1956 industrial economics was added, when the laboratory had developed, in Barnick's words, "a sort of critical mass of technology." Battelle-Columbus was then relatively weak in economics, a field in which Stanford Research Institute had decided to concentrate heavily.

Neither Frankfurt nor Geneva showed any disposition toward growth for growth's sake. In order to maintain quality, Barnick favored growth of not over 5 percent a year. But in order to have a backlog for the early months of the year, when research directors do not yet have their budgets and very little work can be sold, he liked to sell about 10 percent more than his own budgeted commitments.

Some moves were made toward developing other laboratories in Europe. Very early in its overseas explorations, Battelle had taken an option on some property near Versailles, but was held back by lack of cooperation, if not outright obstructionism, on the part of the local authorities. Battelle also flirted with the idea of acquiring the Breda Research Institute in Milan, which had been patterned largely after Battelle itself, but the deal fell through because of opposition from the Italian communists. Williams backed strongly a laboratory in England, and a plan was developed which won the active support of Ramsay MacDonald, then Chancellor of the Exchequer, but the Battelle Board turned Williams down on the ground that it did not favor such expansion.

As the two European laboratories showed themselves able to cover the field adequately, thoughts of starting additional units disappeared, and Frankfurt and Geneva kept expanding their facilities. Frankfurt's growth tended to move in surges, with people being cramped into available space, then spreading out as new buildings were added, then becoming cramped again as the process was repeated. And whereas the laboratory once had to hire competent people from industry, it eventually found that industry would hire from the laboratory, as people would be lost to sponsors "with the final report." These ex-staffers, in turn, knowing Battelle's capabilities, were likely to sponsor more research.

In the choice between what Fawcett has called "proactive" and "reactive" research (and what had once been distinguished as active and passive), Frankfurt tended in its first five years toward the reactive—in which the sponsor brings in his problems and tends to try the laboratory on for size. Since then, it has emphasized proactive research—pushing its own ideas, because these projects usually last longer, hold sales costs down, and are favored by the researchers themselves. Soon, about 50 percent of Frankfurt research became proactive.

Frankfurt's departments include Physics, Chemistry, Biology, Electronics and Computer Sciences, Mechanical Engineering, Materials Science, and Economics. Battelle-Frankfurt is strong in semiconductor work, has done a good deal on solar cells, and has worked on holography, particularly in the application of showing droplet size and distribution in aerosols. It has not moved far into the behavioral sciences, although some long-range regional planning is done, as well as some work on pollution and waste disposal. For German industry, technological planning—industrial planning, technological forecasting, training methods, and long-range planning—is being done. A Battelle man is also on the staff of the Ministry of Research and Education, which is seeking methods of planning priorities in its subsidization and support of government research.

Frankfurt is partial to the kind of high-risk research that is frequently best done under group contracts, with many participating sponsors, although these are usually slow to catch on. Group projects have been conducted on fuel cells and on the long-range future of air freight, for example.

Battelle-Geneva is highly science-oriented, and Thiemann leans strongly toward the scientific community in the work that is done. Like Switzerland itself, the Geneva research center is extremely heterogeneous, its personnel coming from thirty different countries and harboring a great variety of outlooks. A man who meets Thiemann's ideal of researcher-entrepreneur can rise rapidly from technician to head of a project or division, regardless of background or education. About 70 percent of the ideas, including most of those involved in the bigger projects, are generated at the Geneva laboratory, another sign of Thiemann's impress.

Thiemann himself describes his laboratory's operation as covering a broad spectrum of activities in both the soft sciences, which he feels are needed to define what the institute and its sponsors should be doing, and the hard. Each of these has three pyramided levels, ranging from the most theoretical at the apex to the most practical and applied at the base.

Somewhere toward the middle of the hard sciences pyramid fell the considerable amount of work done by Battelle-Geneva in semiconductor technology. Geneva researchers conceived a technique whereby, by vacuum condensation, a thin film coating can be laid down under exquisite control in a monocrystalline manner to become the basis for epitaxial transistors. With fine control of impurities in each layer through vacuum deposition, the result is a system of active and passive elements on a single crystal, producing an integrated circuit. A sponsor was found for this project, which was carried on for thirteen years.

Among the outgrowths of this new technology are an electronic watch, controlled power rectifiers, and a department working on such products as a variable-speed locomotive engine, an inexpensive and easily operated variable-speed asynchronic engine, automobile engines, and a control system for a 100-ton rubber-tired vehicle for open-pit mining. Semiconductors have led also to such continuous transportation systems as a high-speed moving sidewalk, now in the prototype stage in Geneva.

Thiemann himself has a propensity for making things work better. During a 1952-53 visit to the United States, he stayed on the top floor of the New York Athletic Club, close enough to the elevators so that he could observe their antiquated machinery. He decided something better was needed. When he returned to Geneva, he developed a static electronic system for driving and controlling a single elevator or an entire bank. Hundreds of his elevators have since been installed.

As in Germany, Geneva sponsors tend to be the larger companies. Even in economic group projects directed toward long-range planning, the sponsors are large firms with expert economics departments of their own. Battelle-supported studies at Geneva in the physical, life, and social sciences, begun in the mid-60s, point to new areas of sponsored industrial research within two or three years. This research is conducted mainly at the Advanced Study Center, a kind of think tank with a dozen or more theoreticians who develop unorthodox ideas and approaches. Exemplifying this research is the study of active transport across membranes.

As U. S. research has become more pinched for funds in recent years, there has been a kind of reverse brain drain to the Swiss laboratory. These migrating scientists include not only a number of Swiss who earlier departed for the United States, but also several native Americans.

The real significance of Battelle's European operations, according to Thomas, has been the demonstration that American science and technology could successfully be transported out of their parochial shell and spread abroad, even to industrial nations. The experience of Frankfurt and Geneva may well have provided the impetus for the move to Battelle-Northwest.

In 1970 Fawcett had a white paper prepared to project the future of Europe's economy. The conclusion reached was that not only Europe, but Asia as well, may be opening up more and becoming more economically important—indications that it might be wise for Battelle to broaden its overseas base. Indeed, both Geneva and Frankfurt, with total staffs of more than 1,500, operated profitably in 1970, while the U. S. labs slipped into the red.

Around the World

Just as the Europeans have demonstrated that projects need not be confined to their own countries, so have all Battelle laboratories shown a willingness to spread their capabilities around the world.

Battelle has conducted research projects in more than ninety countries. Much of this work involves broad area surveys, industrial feasibility studies, or having Battelle replicate itself on a small scale by setting up research institutes abroad.

As early as 1956, seven Battelle people went to Lebanon, where they spent more than two years establishing a research center known as the Industry Institute of Lebanon. This was a project of the International Cooperation Administration, forerunner to the U. S. Agency for International Development (AID). The Industry Institute, while it has not grown much since that time, is still operating.

Somewhat more promising has been the Korea Institute of Science and Technology (KIST), also sponsored by AID. Begun in 1965, this project made use of Battelle's experience and background to give Korea a start in technological development. Although the Koreans tended to reject simple ideas that they could use and to reach for the more glamorous American technology that they could not, the KIST management has been more realistic. Its director was once heard to tell a candidate for a research job, "If you come to work for me, what you *won't* get is a Nobel Prize." KIST has become deeply involved in industrial activities, and it appears that it will be able to run well on its own momentum.

In 1959-60, Battelle conducted a major study for the Alaska International Rail and Highway Commission to determine transportation needs over the next twenty years, as well as the feasibility of a railroad from Alaska to tie in to feeders and to lines to the U.S. Northwest. Partly because of the high cost of development and the relative ease of building roads to explore possible traffic demands, the study concluded that the economics of a railroad did not make sense. Somewhat similarly, when Turkey judged in 1964 that its future economic growth would require more electric power and planned to invest a substantial sum in a hydroelectric power site in the east-central region, a Battelle team was called in to make a study of the economics of the project. They spent a month making long-term projections of the growth of various power-using industries. Their finding was that the Turks *did* need the additional power to foster healthy growth rates in various industrial areas, and that the planned project was both economically and technologically feasible. The construction went ahead.

When it appeared that Britain would enter the Common Market, New Zealand was in danger of losing an important outlet for its livestock and dairy products. As a consequence, it might be necessary for New Zealand to conserve foreign exchange money by making its own steel, even though this would cost more than importing steel from Japan. Battelle-Columbus has been acting as the technical right hand of the quasi-governmental steel agency since the mid-1960s. New Zealand, it has been found, has black sands rich in magnetite. With this point of entry, Battelle has made other New Zealand studies—on the port of Auckland, on the feasibility of exporting wool tops, rather than unscoured wool, to England, and on the prospects for the world wool market. In one year—1968—Battelle provided metallurgical and economic advice aimed at the establishment of steel mills in five nations—Australia, New Zealand, Korea, Pakistan, and Brazil.

Various regional studies have been sponsored by AID, the World Bank, and others. Battelle has been assigned the supervision of contract work for an economic development study of Iran.

By 1964, BDC joined with fifty-three other organizations in the United States, Canada, Western Europe, and Japan to form the ADELA Investment Company, with a capitalization of $40 million, to provide capital and technical and managerial help to Latin American private enterprise.

All Battelle laboratories have worked around the world. Battelle-Frankfurt has played a role in the mounting volume of German development aid to other countries for a number of years, and has numerous staff members in Asia, Africa, and Latin America. Geneva has some technical projects in Australia, a part of the world that Battelle-Columbus once thought of as its own technological game preserve. The top man in Battelle's Rio de Janeiro office is from Geneva; the top man in Caracas is from Frankfurt.

A recent Frankfurt group project on the merits and limits of fast-firing ceramic products had sponsors from Germany, the Netherlands, Belgium, Denmark, Finland, Norway, Sweden, Switzerland, France, Italy, Spain, England, and Colombia. And the laboratories recognize that the solutions to many of the problems toward which Battelle research is moving at an accelerated rate—pollution, transport, education, urban deterioration—will require not only multidisciplinary, but worldwide, approaches. Says Barnick: "We live in a time when all our sponsors have a multinational outlook."

70

CHAPTER EIGHT

The Diversifying Years

With Xerox money flowing in and the European laboratories self-sustaining, Battelle could, toward the close of the 1950s, afford to do more long-range planning. This had not been true even a few years earlier, because then a steady procession of profitable contracts had been essential to support growth.

As soon as the immediate financial pressure relaxed, the Institute under Thomas could indulge in some intellectual philanthropy. As he once told a reporter: "The technical man has been drawn into the stream of human events . . . in such a way that he has become the custodian of civilization." One of Thomas' first proposals to the Trustees was the establishment of Battelle Institute (BI). It was not to be a new laboratory, he explained, but rather a fund of $1,000,000 a year for exploring fields not yet ripe for contract research. BI, whose appropriation has since swelled to almost $5 million annually, was different from the "maintenance-of-mind" account established by Gillett in that BI funds could be used to hire and support men who might not otherwise join Battelle.

The Institute continued to expand the bread-and-butter practical research on metals and other materials on which it had built its reputation. At the same time it began branching out into many other areas where engineering and science have something to contribute—education, the delivery of medical care, oceanology, regional planning, desert ecology, pollution control, and urban problems, to name just a few.

71

Some diversification had, of course, occurred much earlier, as when men seeking new uses for copper had brought in biochemists and agricultural scientists to help solve specific problems. But until the Thomas regime Battelle's chief interest was to advance hard science, and the harder the better.

Nevertheless, social scientists had in a few instances established footholds through their own initiative. In 1957, for example, engineers building a complex machine had brought in a psychologist versed in human factors of machine design—where to put the controls for maximum convenience and how to make the indicator panels easy to read. After this job was finished, the psychologist stayed on. But rather than continue as an appendage to engineering, he preferred to work on problems that were primarily psychological. No one in management objected, just so long as he went out and sold research contracts, which he did.

Enter Economists

Still, Battelle could not depend on such happenstance if it seriously wanted to diversify into the realm of social problems. It had to use BI funds for seed money. Since the early days engineers had made successful surveys of technology or natural resources that included economic aspects. But Thomas wanted the Institute to become strong in social economics. The first move was to hire bright young men, typically with undergraduate training in economics and masters' degrees in business administration. Turned loose pretty much on their own, the youngsters accomplished little, if anything.

And so the policy was changed. Battelle switched to older men with Ph.D.'s in economics and some business experience. They worked out much better. They were soon able to help hard scientists judge the future relevance of various fields of research. They also generated Aids to Corporate Thinking, a large group research project to which many companies subscribe in order to learn Battelle's analysis of technical and business trends five to fifteen years in the future.

Whether economics research will ever be wholly disassociated from technology is still a question. The answer is "probably not," in the opinion of George James, who served for several years as a Battelle economist and is now a senior vice-president of the Air

72

Transport Association of America. He says: "I can't imagine them attracting a Paul Samuelson or holding him or even knowing what to do with him."

Nevertheless, in economics related to technology, regional development, or other research in the mainstream of Battelle's interests, the Institute now has an enviable reputation. Harvey Brooks, Dean of Engineering and Applied Physics at Harvard, was particularly impressed by a report on the national demand for electricity through the year 2000, which was prepared for the White House Office of Science and Technology. "Naturally, it was a search of the literature," he points out, "but the interpretations were exceptionally shrewd. It represents a real contribution to the social implications of technology." Perhaps Battelle has no reason to divert its efforts into more theoretical research in economics.

Training Trainers to Train

Battelle staked its first claim in the field of education research during the early 1960s, when it gathered a small staff of psychologists skilled in programmed instruction. "Teaching machines" had captured the public's imagination at the time, and several research contracts were promptly sold. One was a program for training salesclerks for a nationwide department store chain. Another trained maintenance men for a cash register company. The Department of Health, Education and Welfare signed a contract to investigate training programs to train people as training supervisors. This was an ideal way to get started in educational research in general. Not only were contracts relatively easy to come by, but results were easily demonstrated: trainees either learned or they didn't, and Battelle's teaching programs were successful.

The Institute's first major research on public education began in 1966 with a study of ninety Ohio school districts, including three Catholic dioceses. William Hitt, who headed the group, admits that the work was highly educational for him and his group—as well as for the sponsors. The central problem was that the school districts had never decided what should be their major objectives, and so the researchers helped them arrive at a consensus: a list of the "thirty most important educational problems" as judged by educators themselves. Near the top were: describing the educational program to the public; negotiating with teachers; setting salary policies and schedules; and evaluating the performance of the school professional staff. On the other hand, most Ohio school boards were little concerned about: policy for student health services; dealing with minority groups on special problems; or planning land acquisition for new facilities.

This study showed the need for a new Center for Improved Education at the Columbus Laboratories, with Battelle committing support for the first five years. Almost as soon as it was announced, the center got more than 100 sponsors: the ninety Ohio school districts, plus fourteen more in Westchester County, New York. In Hitt's view, his job will be analogous to that of a Department of Agriculture County Agent. That is to say, the center will be mainly a clearinghouse to advise clients as to whether they are using the best educational methods available. It will keep an eye out for new developments and will evaluate them, but it will not try to invent them.

Problems of the Cities

Battelle began research in urban affairs at about the time it became active in education research—but more cautiously. Fearing to get embroiled in local politics, Thomas first offered the Institute's services to Cleveland. A group under Joseph Duncan studied a number of specific problems and came up with recommendations on several, including a city income tax, the reduction of pollution from an industrial power plant, and the advisability of handling some functions, such as purchasing school supplies, on a county-wide basis. "We were not always right and not always applauded," says Duncan, "but Battelle's image did not suffer, and so we decided to try the same work in Columbus."

Education and social research today account for about 12 percent of the Columbus Laboratories' work—up from virtually zero a decade ago. Aside from cities and states, with their recurrent financial crises, the only major sponsor is the Department of Health, Education and Welfare. But the Departments of Transportation and of Housing and Urban Development have announced intentions to begin supporting research on a large scale.

Many of the hard scientists at the Institute still look on the social scientists almost as men from another planet. As a noted engineer recently pointed out, problems on the borderline between sociology and technology are not "merely multidisciplinary but undisciplined." One who understands the inherent difficulties is Kaj Nielsen. Formerly an industrial mathematician at Battelle, he began splitting his time between the Institute and the Central Ohio Transit Authority, which serves Columbus and ten smaller cities and towns nearby. "For mathematics getting to the moon and back is straightforward, but transportation is full of uncertainties," Nielsen declares. "Political decisions, not technology, are the toughest part. You can have a 300-mile-an-hour train anytime you want it, but first you have to decide to pay for it."

More Theory for Metallurgists

Even in the hard sciences diversification has been pushed. Almost all the metallurgical work done through the 1950s, including the noteworthy research on titanium, was based on the traditional experimental approach to materials. In order to counterbalance the oldtimers who relied on their lore and cut-and-try experimentation,

Thomas formed a Metal Science Group in 1960. Its objective is to look into the basic physics of metallurgy, some of which may not help solve problems for twenty years or more, and to try to relate phenomena to theory.

As it is, most of the metallurgists are relying more and more on thermodynamic and other calculations to separate solutions that might work from those that are theoretically impossible. Theoretical calculations can greatly limit the number of critical experiments that must be performed. For this reason it is not unusual today to see an engineer dressed in a white shirt, with a sheaf of computer printouts tucked under his arm.

Giant Step Westward

By far the biggest event during the diversifying years was the acquisition of the management contract for the United States Atomic Energy Commission's Hanford Laboratory in Richland, Washington. This had been part of the nation's first plutonium manufacturing center, sprawling over the desert for 640 square miles, an area half the size of Rhode Island.

General Electric, which had run all of Hanford under contract since 1946, withdrew in 1964, and the AEC decided to split its many functions among several different organizations. Battelle was not at all interested in manufacturing fuels, constructing and maintaining buildings, providing bus service, or many of the other tasks that needed to be performed, but it wanted very much to take over Hanford's superlative research laboratory.

The Institute's bid was made partly for defensive reasons, because it had long been one of the AEC's main research contractors and could well use Hanford to maintain that position. The AEC, for its part, was firmly committed to emphasizing peaceful uses of atomic energy and willingly gave Battelle permisison to use the laboratory partly for nongovernment work at a reasonable fee. Battelle cooperated by agreeing to invest $5 million of its own funds in new laboratory buildings and equipment, and this helped clinch the acquisition contract. The following year the Institute announced plans to invest another $20 million over the next decade.

Thus, in one stroke Battelle acquired 1,800 more staff members and a fourth major research center, which it named the Pacific

Northwest Laboratories and organized as part of a new Pacific Northwest Division—commonly referred to as Battelle-Northwest. Only a handful of the former GE engineers and scientists decided not to stay on when Battelle took over.

Battelle-Northwest and Battelle-Columbus might have split U.S. research contracts by drawing a line somewhere down the middle of the country and allocating the west to Northwest, the east to Columbus. Instead, each laboratory has been encouraged to develop its own style and specialties. BNW, for example, has a staff with years of experience in monitoring nuclear wastes, and naturally they have become especially familiar with problems of the environment. They have, for example, started one of the world's leading centers of desert ecology on nearby Rattlesnake Mountain. Recently BNW signed a $167,000 contract to improve wastewater treatment for the city of Cleveland. This was not considered poaching, for Columbus has about $150,000 in contracts in the State of Washington.

Enrichment of the Mind

Thomas had felt all along that Battelle should redouble its efforts to encourage creativity and education in an organized way. Early in his term as director he had established close relationships with the academic world by having Battelle endow professorships and encouraging the interchange of ideas with The Ohio State University, which is just across the street from the Columbus Laboratories. The governor of Ohio reciprocated in 1960 by naming Thomas a trustee of the university.

When Battelle moved into the Pacific Northwest, Thomas urged the Trustees to take a bold further step in this general direction. He wanted to establish a small institution adjacent to the University of Washington campus in Seattle somewhat along the lines of the Institute for Advanced Study in Princeton. The necessary funds were made available, and the Seattle Research Center was built and began operating in 1967.

Like the Institute for Advanced Study, the Center has a nucleus of a few long-term fellows, usually appointed for up to five years. In addition, it has a varying number of visiting fellows (up to twenty-five in the summer months), who stay for periods ranging from a few weeks to a year to work on a project of special importance to their careers. A man may take this interlude to write a book, polish a theory, or acquaint himself with an entirely new field. The emphasis has been on social sciences, but some important thinking has been done in pure mathematics and physics.

Money for running the Center comes partly from Battelle's general funds, partly from BI. It is used to house and feed visitors and also in some cases to supplement their salaries so that their stays will not require any financial sacrifice.

The Seattle Research Center has done much to convince academic scientists that Battelle is a highly respectable scientific organization. Battelle staff members from all four major laboratories get a chance to rub elbows with illustrious scientists at meetings held throughout the year. The most widely known are called *rencontres* (French for "confrontations"). They are attended each summer by fifteen eminent physicists and the same number of mathematicians, who spend six weeks discussing a single topic of interest to men in both areas. Other meetings have bracketed a remarkable range, from international seminars on the frontiers of metallurgical theory to an evaluation of *Sesame Street*. The men who manage the Center point out, a little shyly, that it is also head-quarters for a scientific study group known as the West Coast Sex Society.

The Center has helped to broaden the outlook of many staff members; each year about 10 percent visit Seattle for a few days to several months. Sometimes, though rarely, the experience proves so stimulating that Battelle loses a good man. The prime example is Robert Fuller, a brilliant young theoretical physicist who was also interested in the physiology of the nervous system. He went to Seattle in 1967 to finish a book on quantum physics. But while there he got a chance to teach a highly innovative class in biology to a class of potential dropouts in a nearby high school. He soon became so personally involved with education that he resigned from the Center to become Dean of Faculty at Trinity College and then president of Oberlin College.

Fuller still maintains close ties with several people at Battelle and he remains enthusiastic about the importance of the Seattle Research Center. "It is," he says, "the nose of the dinosaur that smells out fields which will be vital to Battelle in the future."

CHAPTER NINE

Today and Tomorrow

Has Battelle reached its zenith? Do all paths, from now on, lead downward or, at best, sideways? Doom-sayers have been answering these questions affirmatively since the Institute was young. Earl Hayes, chief scientist of the U.S. Bureau of Mines, recalls being told on his first visit to Columbus in 1943 that Battelle was "finally mature." At that time the staff numbered about 400 and had few interests outside of good but conventional metallurgy.

The size of the staff has declined considerably from a peak of 7,000 to about 5,500. But almost all this reduction resulted from a carefully weighed decision to abandon one of the biggest programs in the Institute's history: the management of the so-called Fast Flux Test Facility (FFTF) at Hanford. This is to be a new type of nuclear power reactor using liquid sodium as a coolant. Battelle turned it back to the AEC in mid-1970, because the tax laws of 1969, relating to how much work a not-for-profit organization could do for any one sponsor, put Battelle's tax status as a publicly supported organization in jeopardy. Westinghouse took over management of the FFTF and with it almost all the people who had been working on the project.

Currently, however, newly signed contracts and budding research activities promise to more than offset the loss of the FFTF. A few examples illustrate that the potential for growth is hardly limited.

The National Aeronautics and Space Administration has asked Battelle for a study of man's nutritional needs in space. Starting with information from the Mercury, Gemini, and Apollo missions, scientists will evaluate problems for space stations and trips to distant planets. They will make recommendations on storage, packaging, sanitation, and quality control.

Systems engineers are already planning better ways to route passengers and baggage at several large airports. They are also getting involved in mass transit to and from airports, and for the airlines they are studying ground handling of planes, traffic control, and technical forecasts of needs for staff and equipment. Since every airport presents special problems, parts of these jobs will have to be done over and over again.

The Swiss government and some companies have shown renewed interest in magnetohydrodynamics (MHD), a way of generating electric power by blowing streams of gas and charged particles between pairs of electrodes. A decade ago engineers were enthusiastic about the potential of MHD for cheap power, but the excitement died down because durable materials for electrodes were not available. Now interest is picking up again, owing to recent advances in materials science; Robert Jaffee predicts that $100 million of MHD research will be done in the next ten years. In this field, he says, Battelle is like a stock speculator who decides the market has hit bottom and therefore begins to buy.

Battelle has begun a head-on attack on the zooming costs of health care. A contract for stepping up efficiency is being supported by Blue Cross, the Kellogg Foundation, and a group of hospitals in Washington, Idaho, and Oregon. This is another project that may have to be repeated many times with variations to solve special local problems.

When it was invented a decade ago, the laser was described as "a solution looking for problems." Although some uses have since emerged—cutting materials and attaching detached retina of the eye—the exploitation of lasers has only begun. A new Laser Applications Center in Columbus seems assured of innumerable problems to solve.

The concentration of ores, one of Battelle's earliest specialties, is now more promising than ever. As natural resources are depleted, mining companies are turning to skimpy ores they would have ignored only a few years ago, and these ores must first be concentrated before they can be fed into today's refining processes.

80

Joining Hands with OSU

Battelle reaffirmed its commitment to education—particularly education directed to the welfare of mankind—in April, 1971, when it announced plans for an Academy for Contemporary Problems. The Institute will build the $2 million Academy on a $1\frac{1}{4}$-acre site it owns in Columbus. The mission is to do research on public problems of all kinds, promote the application of knowledge, and provide advanced training. In this venture Battelle and The Ohio State University are fifty-fifty partners; they have agreed jointly to support the Academy with $1 million a year for a minimum of ten years. The first director is Ralph Widner, who formerly served as executive director of the Appalachian Regional Commission.

Another cooperative program under consideration is a study on drug abuse, to be conducted in partnership with The Ohio State University and Riverside Hospital.

Fawcett is confident that Battelle will impart to these and similar ventures a special character derived from its skill in the hard sciences. This quality might be described as an appreciation of the importance of definite numbers—the quantitative approach that the physicist or engineer applies to everything he does. The advent of computers has helped make this approach feasible for some social problems, where there are normally a great many variables interacting over a wide range.

Growing Old Gracefully

Despite the number and variety of fresh opportunities, there is no denying that Battelle has reached a new level of maturity. It is often called upon as a kind of elder statesman to referee projects in which it is not otherwise involved. The U.S. Army, for example, contracted with Battelle to criticize and evaluate almost every detail of the Main Battle Tank program, from design to production planning. The Office of Economic Opportunity is relying on Battelle to measure the success of six of the much talked about commercial companies that are trying experimentally to deliver public education more effectively and at lower cost than local school systems do.

But maturity has engendered some worrisome problems inter-

81

nally. Back in the Williams era it was sometimes said that any man could become a division chief in a hurry if he could bring in $200,000 worth of contracts per year. Battelle still gives more leeway to young people than almost any other organization. One young social scientist recalls the first contract negotiation he attended a few months after he had been on the job. "You know who represented the Institute?" he says. "Me! In the sponsor's eyes I was Mr. Battelle."

Fawcett and others fear, however, that very able youngsters who deserve to rise rapidly because of talent and enterprise now find that higher levels of the organization have little room for them. Indeed, a superannuated senior staff could be detrimental, unless the Institute grows rapidly. A possible solution may be to start the additional European, and perhaps Asian, laboratories suggested in Fawcett's 1970 white paper.

Social scientists have a special complaint. Not one of them is very near the top of the organization, and some of them feel resentful. For many years the Board of Trustees has consisted of three Ohio businessmen and three physical scientists. The balance may be altered by the arrival on the scene of William McChesney Martin, Jr., former president of the New York Stock Exchange and long-time Chairman of the Federal Reserve Board. Famous for his energy and outspokenness, Martin was elected an Associate Trustee in 1970.

Fawcett and his top associates hope that through growth or reorganization or both Battelle will recapture its reputation as a place where no job is a dead end. This may prove one of the most difficult problems the Institute has ever attempted. A highly respected alumnus, William Harris, left a few years ago to become vice-president of the American Association of Railroads, because he felt that he could rise no higher at Battelle until people above him quit or died. "What the Institute needs," he says, "is a year-long project to study itself. Take BI money and support ten to fifteen really top-rate people. Let them devote fulltime to doing research on research."

Yet in its present stage of maturity Battelle has shown none of the tendencies of old men to pontificate or elderly scientists to speculate about leisurely blue-sky solutions to pressing problems. Like a youngster, it lives in the here and now, and this delights Trustee John Pierce. Recently retired from Bell Telephone Lab-

82

oratories to an engineering professorship at Cal Tech, Pierce applauds rugged, though perhaps untidy, solutions. He believes the Institute should stay just ahead of the problems of the times, the crises, the headlines. He explains: "Engineering progress usually starts with crude, realistic solutions. Then science follows. An example is aerodynamics, which followed the airplane and refined it."

A recent small project best illustrates what Pierce and other people admire most in Battelle. The problem was to design a simple water pump that AID would distribute to villagers in India. Thousands of pumps, of course, are on the market, but this one had to meet extraordinary specifications. As many as 300 people would have to rely on it night and day for all their water. It had to fit both deep and shallow wells, and it had to be maintainable by unskilled workers with simple tools.

The solution was a rough-and-ready pump of exquisitely simple design and construction. It has a low-cost, corrosion-resistant cylinder and a bare minimum of threaded fasteners. The casting, lightly machined, can easily be turned out by small factories with few power tools. In short, it is an ideal engineering solution for a developing country.

CHAPTER TEN

The Business of Battelle

Although Battelle Memorial Institute was organized on a not-for-profit basis, there was every intention of running it as a not-for-loss institution as well. Gordon Battelle's will had anticipated the possibility of earnings by specifying that a part of the Institute's net income should go to such worthwhile purposes as "will do the greatest good for humanity."

Operations in the earliest days were not on a scale that would tend to result in much net income—or any at all. Total expenditures on research in 1930, the first full calendar year of activities, amounted to just $71,000. Batelle was unlike such organizations as the Mellon Institute in that this income had to support a permanent staff that grew in size as research projects grew in diversity. By 1931, the staff numbered some fifty people, which included a heavy concentration in research scientists and technicians.

The level of research operations was such that there was a drain on the endowment in the early years. By 1934 the Institute's volume of research contracts had risen to $173,000. But the staff had expanded further by then, to almost 100. Not until the early 40s did the Institute receive a net income from its contract research operations.

Gillett was not one to be perturbed by the lack of financial progress, as long as he knew that the Institute was doing good work and that its reputation for technical excellence was being

85

enhanced. But for Williams this was not enough. He had in mind a vision of growth for Battelle Memorial Institute that the income from the endowment could not begin to finance. It was a vision he started to turn into a reality as soon as he and Gillett changed job titles.

Williams Takes Over

In the early days, Battelle had virtually no competition. There were some commercial consulting laboratories, such as Arthur D. Little, Inc., but they were busiest in other areas. The Mellon Institute was more of a fellowship arrangement conducted in collaboration with industry. University personnel did very little consulting work at the time, and in any event tended to steer clear of practical problems. But Battelle's people, although held in high regard in scientific circles, had come mostly from industry, the National Bureau of Standards, or the Bureau of Mines, and they were known for their feet-on-the-ground approach to research.

With all the elements of a clearcut monopoly at his fingertips, Williams still had his selling job cut out for him. Industry generally had not yet begun to think of research as an activity to which to commit any significant fraction of its money or resources. Even those companies that invested in research preferred to gear it closely to their own organizations and products. And the pall that the Depression had cast over industry should have been enough to discourage any sensible person coming along with something new in the way of business expense.

Williams was neither insensible nor discouraged. He simply decided that if there was a difficult direct selling job to do, it would have to be done. Outgoing, dynamic, convinced of the value of research, and capable of passing some of his own fire along to others, he was a superb salesman for Battelle's product. But he was also a realist, prepared not only for the difficulties of selling Battelle as an institution but also those of selling the very idea of having research done competently and efficiently outside of industry's own walls.

Partly to make it more palatable, Williams invented a term for it: contract research. A. D. Little had done jobs for industry, mainly in chemistry, in this manner, but called it "process development." Even Battelle itself had been doing work of this kind,

86

known as "sponsored" projects, but it was Williams who expanded the idea into a concept and then sold it on the outside. As a consequence, Battelle also pioneered in forming teams of individuals —or, when necessary, fractions of individuals—to concentrate on projects within a single discipline or across disciplines.

The metals industries, where Battelle's early expertise centered, was extremely difficult to break into, and the fuels industry, severely hit by the Depression, was almost impossible. But Williams did not share the inhibitions of most technical people, and he headed directly for the top corporate offices; he enjoyed these associations, and Battelle profited from them.

Gillett encouraged him in these forays, but sometimes proved a greater impediment to new business than the sponsor himself. "I'd get some corporation interested in a research project," Williams recalls, "and Gillett would question whether we ought to take their money or not. It was sometimes harder to sell Gillett on a project than it was the industrial concern."

Gillett and Williams nevertheless made a remarkably compatible team. Gillett would develop research ideas, and write papers on them. Williams would then arrange to see the individual in a company who might be interested, and then go on to see the top operating executive, usually the president. Williams found that business executives felt complimented by a visit from a scientist, and would welcome the association. He used the opportunity to urge them to hire top research men and to make them responsible executives, knowing that Battelle could only gain by helping instill research-mindedness into industry.

The executive suite remained a mystery to most of the other top people at Battelle, even those, like Gillett, Clarence Lorig, Oscar Harder, Byron Bird, Bruce Gonser, Clarence Sims, A. C. Richardson, and others, with national or international reputations in the fields of metals and minerals. Richardson recalls walking around the block three times before screwing up enough courage to visit officials of a Pittsburgh steel company to sell them on the idea of sponsoring a project.

But in time, industry itself took on more technical people, who in turn were familiar with the kind of capabilities Gillett had developed at Battelle. Industrial research and development was anything but sophisticated at the time. Metallurgists in industry had many problems, but usually lacked both the time and the equipment to seek solutions. So in the relatively small world of top people with practical knowledge in these fields, they would meet and talk shop with Battelle's research engineers, comparing problems and swapping ideas. Williams would encourage such associations, and they became a major source of sponsored projects for Battelle.

The Air of a Business

Under Gerald Fenton as business manager, Battelle Memorial Institute developed those business and administrative functions that the fledgling organization needed—personnel, physical facilities, accounting, and so on.

At the start, the personnel function was simply a matter of hiring, and most of this was done by Gillett, who called on people he knew or had heard of to join Battelle. Russell Drum became the first personnel supervisor, running an office that was concerned primarily with hiring, but which also administered a few employee benefits. The function expanded gradually into the more complex areas of staff relations, counseling, developmental education, health and safety services, pensions, and minority recruiting. But, throughout, the technical staff has always played a major role in the recruiting and selection of new professionals and technicians.

The man who was very early put in charge of physical facilities was Bill Welcker, hired on September 1, 1929, a young mechanical engineer who had been in power plant work and railroad management during the three years since he had been out of school. At the time the Institute was housed in what is now the north section and west wing of the King Avenue Building, or Building A. Welcker was made responsible for all purchasing, building maintenance and, in time, new construction. As the Institute grew, he took charge of the physical testing laboratory, the heat treating laboratory, the metallographic laboratory, the photographic laboratory, first aid facilities, general utility functions, and visitor reception and guidance. In 1937, when Battelle was starting to construct Building 1, its second large building, Welcker was put in charge of all physical facilities, as an assistant to Fenton.

Given the requirements for any new construction, Welcker was able to visualize the complete structure, with all its functional characteristics. As Battelle continued to grow, so did its physical plant at Columbus, from 79,000 square feet at the start to 169,000 by 1940, 488,000 by 1950, and 982,000 by 1970. Eventually it reached approximately 1,250,000 square feet on what grew from a 3-acre site to some 38 acres for the Columbus Laboratories alone, in addition to some 100,000 square feet on 400 acres of what had been farmland at the West Jefferson site in nearby Madison County. Welcker also took charge of wartime priorities, serving on a variety of government boards, and he set up the wartime security system that has been maintained ever since.

Growth also brought new problems in financial controls and administration. Not long after Williams became director, he hired Ernst Seckendorff, who had been educated in Germany but had been in the United States for about twenty years, as an administrative assistant. His first assignment was to develop a cost accounting system to help determine the allocation of a multitude of small charges to the appropriate accounts. The new accounting plan enabled the Institute to determine costs of individual projects, and to keep overhead costs down. Seckendorff also established a system for both financial and operating control for the various divisions and departments. This proved so impressive to defense agencies, in connection with government-sponsored research during and after World War II, that defense officials had other research agencies adopt Battelle's accounting practices.

As the Institute grew in size and the accounting functions became more complex, Williams assigned Bert Thomas as an assistant to Seckendorff. Although Thomas had been taken on as a chemist, he had had experience in accounting with a commercial firm in the state of Washington. Thomas took on the full responsibility for this area when Seckendorff left. Before long he was made an assistant director and, in 1957, Director and President of the Institute.

David Minton, who was hired by Williams just before World War II and who spent most of the war years in Washington as an administrative officer of the War Metallurgy Committee, came back to Battelle as assistant to the director after VE Day. Minton became an assistant director soon afterward, vice-president of the Institute in 1955, and director of Battelle Columbus in 1964. Another research engineer who got into administrative work was Edward Slowter, first in 1937 as a part-time liaison man between the patent attorneys and the technical people. After wartime work with the Bell Telephone Laboratories, Slowter returned to Battelle after VJ Day and within a year was spending full time on administrative work, responsible at first for contracts and eventually in charge of all business office operations and nontechnical areas.

For all its businesslike air, Battelle Memorial Institute was never quite like a business. For one thing, its devotion to excellence was implicit in its charter and character rather than imposed by its market. For another, its underlying mission called for a continuing flow of activity, much like that of a foundation, but its service to business and industry had an ebb and flow that corresponded with economic cycles. A research director for a company would generally know his total budget at the start of the year; Battelle knew what some of its budget might be, perhaps half, but had to expend at least part of its efforts scrambling for the rest. "In contract research," said one Battelle man, "you have a goal, rather than a budget." When a major source of sponsorship had its funds restricted, as periodically happened in the case of government research, a Battelle department or division would be hard put to achieve such a goal.

In still other ways, Battelle was very unlike a business. Key members of the staff were professionals, who tend to be cut to their own patterns. Their motivation has always been the solution of problems—not necessarily for profit, but usually within reasonable economic parameters.

Finally, while survival is important to Battelle, as it must be to every vital institution or living organism, a strong sense of competition is not necessarily its best route to survival. Williams helped found The RAND Corporation, and sat on its board. He helped with the initial organization of Stanford Research Institute, and was active in its search for a director. He helped teach the magic of contract research to the Southwest, Southern, Illinois and Midwest Institutes, and Battelle has acted as a major sponsor in helping Midwest to set new patterns for the work that can be done by a regional institute. All these things have been done as though they were part of what BMI was established to do—and in the broadest sense, they are.

Modern Business Principles

For more than a decade after Battelle began operations, its executives had little trouble in getting to know all the staff members or in keeping current on all of the Institute's ongoing projects. But by 1942 the staff had grown to 350, and for the first time project income totaled more than $1,000,000. About 75 percent of this amount went into direct execution of the projects and the remainder to overhead—administrative staff, sales, depreciation, in-house projects, and a special account that Gillett had initiated, known as "M. of M." That stood for "maintenance of the mind," and involved the work done by staff members simply to explore embryo ideas and to keep abreast of what was happening in their fields.

There was a basic scientific rationale in keeping up with what was newest in the researcher's specialty, but there was also an important business purpose in remaining current—and even, in the imagination, in moving ahead. Battelle always tended to hire people who were highly motivated in doing research, and then taught them the blunt facts of life in the contract research business. It was fine to have ideas and imagination, but it was equally important for each division to have enough sponsored work to support its staff. So everyone was inculcated with the need to sell. When a researcher decided what new developments were about to be born, he asked himself who might benefit from them and then talked to someone in the right company. Like any good salesman, it was important for the research engineer to know who would be the right man to see.

Even some of the most highly theoretical scientists found themselves spending 25 percent or more of their time in such selling activities, as they sought to develop work to support their own divisions. Not everyone had to be a salesman. The individual who was constitutionally averse to selling could always find a niche for himself at Battelle, and there were always some who confined their spheres of activity to the laboratory and office.

But scientists come in every stripe and variety. There were others who, like Williams, enjoyed the man-to-man contact that salesmanship provides. One of these was Vern Schnee, a natural salesman and promoter, who brought in a large volume of business from government and industry. He became head of the Project Development Department, which concentrated on getting new contracts, and Minton became his assistant and later his successor.

What developed was a team system, or a two-tier method, of selling. At one level was the man in the laboratory, who had ideas, who was familiar with the state of the art, and who had standing in his professional field. But the world was not beating a path to his door to find out what he was doing. So Project Development people had to go out and ring doorbells, circulate through companies, make up shopping lists of current or projected problems, and get company executives to come and visit Battelle. These salesmen could describe successes and sell the institution. But the step that clinched most sales was taken by the people on the job, who could describe what they were doing and why.

There were some important functions, however, for which the Project Development staff (known as "190-people," after the number of the account to which their activities were charged) were particularly well equipped. They tended to be more familiar with the sponsor's business and had a better sense of what he needed and wanted from research. One job of the department was to maintain a kind of industrial intelligence function, to find out which company was doing what, what the current problems were, and who might listen receptively to the things that the laboratory men were thinking of doing. And because management people turn over at a relatively high rate, it was important to have people at Battelle who worked at renewing the Institute's exposure to sponsors and potential sponsors.

In some important ways, the salesmen and the men in the laboratory have much in common. Both are motivated by enthusiasm, both need the courage of their convictions, and both must have the ability to accept successes and failures in stride. A good research man's successes are most often built on a series of failures, as are the triumphs of a good salesman. Both must empathize with the sponsor, particularly when things begin to go wrong on a project and the customer starts to recall the qualms he had when he signed the contract. Says Project Development's "Mike" Nestor, "You're spending jealous money all the time."

Project Development picked up the group research project idea that Battelle had used almost from the start and formalized it. Battelle would develop a project in which a group of companies in an industry might be interested, and invite key people in those companies to a formal presentation. Each company that decided to join in sponsorship would pay the same amount toward financing the project. This egalitarian arrangement reassured the smaller participants that Battelle, rather than one or two of the large sponsors, would exercise complete control of the research. Patents and licensing would be shared by all sponsors, and antitrust implications would be cleared in advance. Such projects would have to be well thought out, and involve developments with a high degree of feasibility and economic value. Most of the companies invited would usually join in sponsorship. "You guys are a bunch of bandits," one executive once told Minton. "We can't afford to stay out of it."

Group projects have been successfully carried out in a variety of fields—some strictly technical, but most of them heavily weighted with economics. One of the earliest, launched before World War II, was a study of how low-grade ore might best be "beneficiated" so that it could be used to make iron and steel. A recent ambitious group study was a survey of energy sources and requirements for the steel industry through the rest of this century. On the strictly technical side, Battelle made a group evaluation of fuel cells of all types, from those to be used in space capsules to some that might utilize ordinary hydrocarbon fuels for central power station electricity.

Some groups involve only a half-dozen or so sponsors, but one carried out by Battelle-Frankfurt found no fewer than 428 companies interested in learning what Battelle had to say about "Marketing Methods and Problems in the Industrial Capital Goods Industry." Paradoxically, although the group project was conceived largely to help small industries participate in big research projects, most subscribers tend to be large companies with capable research staffs of their own.

As far back as the late 1930s, Battelle made a practice of studying its own business operation. A coordination group studied economic and technical trends and looked at various parts of the overall operations. They examined the rate at which proposals were accepted, and in this way helped make people aware that a certain number of proposals would have to be out most of the time to assure that people in a division or department would have work to do.

The first efforts to apply principles of management science to Battelle's operations were made in the early 1950s, but these were all but given up over the next decade. Some very impressive-looking curves were generated, in order to project volume of activity at the

Institute, but these became virtually meaningless after money began pouring in from the Xerox development. In time, however, the curves and projections began to make sense again.

Battelle now has a marketing program that involves computerized data studies. All government work is cumulated by individual agencies, and non-federal-government work is broken down into five large market areas: the top 50 and 100 next largest industrial sponsors—all of them repeaters; trade associations and technical societies; group research programs; state and local government work; and international work, for either foreign companies or governments. Computerization makes it possible to print out a monthly record of proposals submitted, accepted, rejected, or still outstanding, so that actual business can readily be compared with goals. As expected, the data reveal that more funds are now available in the soft sciences area, and that there is a drop in Atomic Energy Commission funding of projects. Contrary to expectations, they show that the business curve with NASA is going up, even though the agency's funds are more constricted. Says Ed Graves, who is involved with this program, "It keeps you from spinning your wheels and spending your money where there's no market."

To Grow or Not to Grow

A research institute, like a business, is constantly faced with the problem of how much growth to seek, or whether it should grow at all. It had long been said of Williams that he wanted Battelle to be the biggest research institute and of Gillett that he wanted it to be the best. Both judgments were excessively simplistic. Without excellence, it is all but impossible to grow in the research business; without at least a degree of growth, it is almost impossible to acquire the facilities and attract the people that are needed to assure excellence. Still there was enough essential truth in the generalization that both men might have agreed to it.

Battelle's growth was relatively slow during the depressed 1930s, but still rapid enough to enable the Institute to branch out into a number of new disciplines. During the war growth was much more rapid, as research began to come into its own. Williams had been consistently successful in getting the Board to approve funds for new buildings in this period. But when he requested a major new building after the war, R. C. Allen, then President of the Board, told him: "I don't think you should grow any more."

"Why not?" asked Williams. Allen answered: "I don't think the Board could take care of your people in the event of a depression." Replied Williams: "By the time another depression comes along, we will have had enough income from BDC to take care of it." The Board gave him his building.

Research spending continued to grow in the postwar years, and Battelle's operations kept expanding in a number of directions. The Institute underwent some belt-tightening in the mid-1950s, when a government cutback in spending, especially for military purposes, coincided with a minor business recession. But shortly afterwards Xerox money began to pour in, ending Battelle's period of limited capital. Even without Xerox, however, Battelle might have had a net worth of $25 to $30 million, and thus be the best-endowed of all the not-for-profit research institutes.

But the Xerox funds provided great impetus for the growth of Battelle. By 1964 the Institute's research expenditures rose to $39 million, or more than ten times the original endowment that had been put to work 35 years earlier. The following year research expenditures more than doubled, with the full-year operation of the Pacific Northwest facilities, to $86 million. Contract research expenditures then climbed further to $94 million in 1966 (when the total of all sponsored research since Battelle started passed the $500 million mark), to $114 million in 1967, $121 million in 1968, and $125 million in 1969, before slipping back to $110 million in 1970, in a new period of research stringency in both government and industry.

In the final analysis, Battelle's record of growth is perhaps less a matter of conscious decision than one of society's need for the work it does and can do, as well as one of the setting of priorities. When the Institute first came into existence, it filled a pressing need for industry and society, but one that industry was indifferently prepared to recognize. There is still an obvious and real need for independent research organizations to which industry and government can turn when they need an unbiased evaluation of a process or a detached approach to a problem. More and more, these are situations that require a diversity of expertise that only a few organizations like Battelle are equipped to give. As long as American society retains its present orientation, there will almost certainly be a need for a Battelle Memorial Institute, and there will in all likelihood be some need for it to grow.

CHAPTER ELEVEN

Men Who Helped Make Battelle

From its inception, Battelle Memorial Institute had an active, interested Board of Trustees. Until construction and staffing had started, the Board was the only key link between Gordon Battelle's wishes as expressed in his will and the reality of the research laboratory. But even after the Institute was in being, the Board tended to dominate its function and direction in the first years.

In a sense, this was to be expected. The Board had created something in a kind of vacuum; it knew best its own intentions in implementing the will, and it had hired a director to execute those intentions. It was also Horace Gillett's nature to let the Board set the Institute's policies, as long as he was left free to set its professional standards and tone.

Even at that time it would not have been amiss to characterize Gillett as the dean of American metallurgists. He had once worked for Thomas Edison, and he shared some of the great inventor's remarkable ingenuity. And he had accumulated an extraordinary knowledge of alloys and processes.

Gillett went to work for the U.S. Bureau of Mines as chief alloy chemist, and its expert in electric furnaces, alloys, and metallurgy. The Bureau set up experiment stations around the country, and Gillett was put in charge of two World War I projects at Cornell University: the conversion of America's low-grade manganese deposits into ferromanganese for the steel industry, and turning out

97

the nation's first truly high-alloy, iron-based metal for liners of big guns. It was there that Clyde Williams, as a young graduate in chemical engineering, first came to work for Gillett, in 1916. Both projects had limited success, but neither had undergone major development by the time the war ended.

When he first came to the attention of the Battelle Board as a possible director of the new laboratories, Gillett was chief of the metallurgy division of the National Bureau of Standards. Gerald Fenton, who was charged with screening the candidates, went to see him, finding him charming but almost slovenly. Subsequently Gillett arrived in Columbus to be interviewed. With almost total disregard for his personal appearance, he nevertheless charmed the Trustees, too, and they hired him. It was a step none of them would ever regret.

The Gillett Ambience

Gillett undoubtedly had the notion that he would operate the Institute from the income of the endowment, carrying on high-quality research under impeccable professional standards. But he also had a practical turn that made him lean away from the purely theoretical and toward research that could be usefully applied.

Gillett always demanded excellence, from himself as well as others. He brought to Battelle many of the high-caliber scientists he had known at the Bureau of Mines and the Bureau of Standards —Bruce Gonser, Ralph Sherman, Clarence Lorig, Gus Pray, Oscar Harder, and Clyde Williams, who in turn sent for Byron Bird, A. C. Richardson, Clarence Sims, and John Sullivan. These were competent men, whose work was sound, giving the Institute a strong professional underpinning right at the start. Their own instincts matched Gillett's insistence on integrity. His attitude, as one research engineer expressed it, was: "You call the shots the way they are, and as long as you are technically correct, it doesn't matter whether the sponsor is happy or not."

Slight of build, but wiry, he had remarkable stamina. His mind was quick, far-ranging, and incredibly retentive. His own intellectual honesty was buttressed with a sure eye for bluster or affectation in others. But he also possessed a warm humanity and a passion for letting people be themselves. With these qualities he might have become something of a legend, except that the actual facts outdid most fiction.

He was a voluminous and lightning-fast reader, and his mind took in, assembled, and stored all the great variety of things that he read. *Gone With the Wind* he finished in four two-hour evening sessions. He read scientific journals insatiably, and was familiar with what was new and developing in a broad range of technologies. Whatever he read he could call forth on demand. "I always managed to spend a half hour or an hour a week with him," one early associate recalls, "because I could then get the equivalent of all the reading I needed to do." For others, he would make notations on articles—or on advertisements—that he thought would interest them. Or he might refer them, by issue and page, to something he had read a year or two earlier.

He also read and digested a considerable volume of reports written by his colleagues. Because he was quick to find errors of both fact and grammar, people at Battelle learned to be careful in their writing. He would pounce on such wayward syntax as "the data shows," and in the margin he would press a rubber stamp that read, "kittens is." He might point out, "Last month you wrote so-and-so. Why are you changing it?"

Gillett also wrote prodigiously and remembered all that he wrote. In addition to his work at Battelle, he edited *Metals and Alloys,* and his editorials on a wide range of technical matters were frequently regarded as stylistic triumphs. As might be expected, he was the author of a small library of books and manuals.

A pair of scissors sometimes appeared to be his only memory aid. Visitors would often see him combing lean fingers through his hair, and then cutting any wisp that protruded. The result was a close, but sometimes uneven, crewcut. But when the scissors had done their mnemonic duty, he would set them down and send to the library stacks for the right issue of the right journal.

Most of those who knew Gillett carry with them a picture of his ever-present pipe, filled with Serene tobacco and sometimes nestling in his lap as he sat at his desk; the English setters that were so often his companions; and the baggy sweater that was his trademark. The dogs accompanied him on treks across fields and fences, when he would invite hunting partners in relays—one for the morning and one for the afternoon—wearing them out as he went indefatigably on. The dogs would also share the use of the back seat of his beat-up old car with any visiting dignitaries that Gillett might kindly offer to chauffeur around. Gillett's general appearance led one new secretary to mistake him for the janitor and to admonish him for not emptying her wastebasket regularly. He dutifully emptied it.

Gillett loved his work, stayed at it until he retired in 1949, and was a frequent visitor at the laboratories afterwards. When he died in 1950, his mark was nowhere and everywhere at the Institute. Battelle had grown far beyond his own conception, but it was Gillett's indispensable contribution that had laid the foundation for growth.

The Great Builder

It would be difficult to find two people more different in temperament than Horace Gillett and Clyde Williams. Yet what made it possible for the two to work together so smoothly and well was not so much their complementary attributes as their ability to appreciate each other's strengths.

Williams was outgoing, an inveterate salesman, a meeter and greeter. He loved the sound and the feel and the smell of the executive office and the boardroom. He understood business and businessmen, and he knew instinctively what moved, motivated, and impelled them. Many at Battelle, with limited understanding of his capabilities, simply classified him as a promoter or "public relations guy." But he was much more. Williams was a marketing man at a time when the term was little known and less understood. He possessed a deep understanding of what Battelle had to sell and a sound sense of what the customer wanted or should want to buy.

Gillett was aware of his own lack of these capabilities and he recognized them in Williams. Gillett had hardly accepted the new post when, in July, 1929, he wrote to ask Williams to be his assistant. But Williams was then technical adviser and assistant to the president of a steel firm in Utah, and had his heart set on becoming a steel industry executive. He told Gillett he was not interested, but agreed to stop by for a visit during a trip to Pittsburgh in August. Gillett took him to a meeting of the Battelle Board, and got them to approve Williams for the job, which he promptly turned down. But back in the West, told by a banker that a major depression was coming, Williams gave the matter—and his own family situation—second thought. He wired Gillett that he wanted the job, got a confirmation by return wire, and sold his house in a fast-dropping real estate market just before the Wall Street crash.

Gillett, uncomfortable with businessmen—including those on his own Board—immediately made Williams his outside contact man and brought him along to board meetings as his backstop. When Gillett would request an appropriation for new equipment or another research man, he would invariably be asked, "What will be the result of all this, Doctor?" Gillett would reply, "Well, we'll get a paper." Then a Board member would ask, "But can you make any money out of it?" To which Gillett would quickly respond, "No, making money is not the purpose of this." Then, as the board members began to clear their throats, Williams would step in and say, "Now, look, Gillett wants to get us into the corrosion business. And some day, industry will recognize us as authorities and give us research projects. And that's how we'll get a payoff." The Board would approve the request.

No one was happier than Gillett when Williams took over in 1934, a switch that was a *fait accompli* by the time the Board was asked to approve it. The two men exchanged offices and, after a few minutes, Williams heard a hearty laugh from his colleague in the other room. Recalls Williams: "I realized then that I hadn't heard him laugh for a year or two."

Williams first concentrated his energies on selling more research contracts, a move that the more ambitious members of the research staff realized would expand both the available funds and the scope of their interest. Then he turned his attention toward shaping Battelle into his own image of how it should be run. He became the executive, the maker of all key decisions. To help him with his outside relationships, he asked to be put on the Board, a request that was soon granted. In his first year on the job, he started Battelle Development Corporation to prove the utility of good ideas.

Almost singlehandedly, Williams began to let the world—especially the business world—know about Battelle. When the nation's defense effort got under way, Williams directed his attention toward Washington, which began to give Battelle important research contracts. Williams was himself sought out to discuss the nation's critical manganese situation by R. C. Allen, first vice-president of the Oglebay-Norton Company and a geologist of some note, and by C. K. Leith, a University of Wisconsin professor of economic geology then voluntarily advising the Office of Production Management. Williams was put in charge of a Manganese Committee, which Leith soon made a part of the National Academy of Sciences, then headed by Frank Jewett, Chairman of the Board of the Bell Telephone Laboratories.

As the defense emergency turned into the war effort, other committees were formed—on the conservation of tin, copper, aluminum oxide, and other critical materials. As was related in Chapter Four, Williams formed the War Metallurgy Committee to place over the smaller committees, and tapped Zay Jeffries, a General

Electric vice-president, to serve as its vice chairman. Not only did many important government and business figures get to learn more about Battelle, but Williams eventually got Jewett and Jeffries to serve on the Battelle Board; Allen was already a member.

As might have been expected, Williams set Battelle on an essentially pragmatic course. He believed that the Institute's research should be a little ahead of industry, but only a little. He had a basic honesty in dealing with sponsors, and he would not accept even a large contract if he thought Battelle could not deliver. He felt it would help Battelle with business if he were given the title of president, a kind of honorary post that had been held by various Board members, including Fenton, and the Board acceded to his request in 1952.

Internally, as Battelle grew, he reorganized the fifty-some divisions into seven departments, and met weekly with the department heads, as the technical directors group. He encouraged competition among staff members, and the building of small empires that might grow into large ones. Many a division chief got his job because he was able to sell research in a new area and to demonstrate that it had enough stability to be self-sustaining. Williams made his own most logical successors a triumvirate of assistants: Thomas in charge of administration, Crout as head of BDC and personnel, and Vern Schnee—later succeeded by Minton—responsible for sales.

If Williams had one great weakness, it was his inability to draw a sharp line of separation between his inside and outside interests. He lent himself enthusiastically in helping organize The RAND Corporation and Stanford Research Institute. He not only sold research contracts to corporations, but advised them with regard to research, and felt that he should be permitted to serve on their boards.

To Williams, seizing these advantages represented the natural rewards of sound business thinking and acumen. Members of the Board did not share this belief. The philosophical impasse was great enough so that Williams submitted his resignation, and it was accepted by the Board. He continued to serve as a trustee for the next year, meanwhile organizing his own highly successful private consulting firm based in Columbus.

But his legacy was clearly visible. He had done much to teach industry the value of research. Nationally and internationally, he had put Battelle on the map, expanding its resources and capabilities to the point where it was easily the world's largest independent research organization.

A New-Horizons Man

The Battelle Board might have been at a loss in choosing a member of the triumvirate to succeed Williams, but there was at least a plausible interim solution in naming Thomas. He had been acting director when Williams was away during the war and Williams had later placed a large part of the Institute's administrative responsibilities on his shoulders. The understanding was that Thomas was to take over for a year or so, working with an executive committee consisting of Crout, Minton, and Ed Slowter.

But Thomas took charge firmly, and so impressed the Board that they soon dropped the interim designation. After three years, he felt strong enough to dissolve the executive committee and to end the practice of having them sit in on Board meetings. In that period Battelle Memorial Institute had clearly felt the impress of the new personality at its head.

That personality marked a return to the intellectual emphasis of the Gillett era. Thomas was thoughtful, scholarly, quiet. But he was also inventive and compassionate; knowing how to use his hands and how things worked, he could relate to anyone in the Institute, and was on a first-name basis with workmen as well as with men in the laboratories. A firm believer that science should pay a debt to society, he nevertheless supported research simply to find new knowledge, and in this way he directed Battelle toward exploring new horizons. Going abroad and developing a new kind of research entity in the Northwest were essentially his ideas.

With a Ph.D. in physical chemistry, Thomas had been hired by Williams in 1934 to help start a chemistry department. But his background soon thrust him into other work. Not only was he a competent scientist, but he had worked for a foundry company in the Northwest, including a stint as assistant auditor. Williams asked Thomas to be his assistant, taking care of such matters as patents, budgets, and financial controls. Thus, once marked as a capable administrator, he was never able to escape those duties.

As President, he began to take steps that would lead to increasing the technical stature of the Institute. He encouraged and fi-

104

nanced fundamental research, and sought to strengthen the staff. He took emphasis away from growth. He had come to Battelle when the staff numbered about 100 and had taken over as President when there were more than 2,500. He started to clean out deadwood and to make hiring more selective, so that his early moves resulted in a reduction in staff size.

Although a capable administrator, Thomas was not interested in administrative detail. He asked the departments to run their own shows. And he put into effect a plan whereby the four laboratories could operate with a large degree of autonomy, as though they were components of a large corporation. To help develop Battelle's organizational structure, he made Sherwood Fawcett his executive vice-president in 1967.

Not much interested in selling, Thomas let the Institute's sales function take care of itself. At Board meetings, during business discussions that did not interest him, he would doodle mathematical abstractions, toying, for example, with Goldbach's Conjecture.* He was unimpressed with the trappings of power and authority. Battelle alumnus Hugo Johnson recalls that Williams would almost invariably lunch with influential businessmen at the exclusive Union Club when he came to Cleveland or at the Duquesne Club in Pittsburgh; but the first time Johnson saw Thomas in Cleveland during the lunch hour, the Battelle President was window-shopping on Euclid Avenue.

Thomas was much concerned with matters relating to his staff, and he got them to write papers, to become involved in community affairs, and to express themselves as individuals. To encourage meetings, seminars, talks, and concerts, he had an auditorium built at Columbus, along with conference rooms. He was interested not only in the relationship of his staff to the academic community, but in Battelle's relationship to its own physical community.

Thomas felt that Battelle should take more positions in the research it conducted, rather than end its projects by giving away all patents and rights to sponsors. He wanted increased emphasis

---

* The Conjecture: Every even number is the sum of two prime numbers, i.e., numbers that cannot be evenly divided by any number smaller than themselves, other than 1. Thus, $2 = 1 + 1$; $10 = 7 + 3$; $342 = 337 + 5$; $47,602 = 47,543 + 59$, etc. Proposed by a mathematical dilettante in 1742, the conjecture has never been proved or disproved.

105

on the establishment of scientific beachheads. To this end, he made himself the prime mover behind the establishment of Battelle Institute, his personal vision of what research could do when it was undiluted by the economic motivations of contract research. But his real accomplishment was something larger—the demonstration that Battelle Memorial Institute should remain a step ahead of society in looking for new directions that research might take, and in moving in some of those directions.

The Fawcett Years

As Thomas approached retirement age, he was called on to play a central role in the choice of a successor. Some Board members felt strongly that an effort should be made to find a man of stature on the outside, probably a scientist from the academic world. Thomas actually interviewed several such candidates.

"But the more I got into it," he says, "the more I began to feel the transformation from the Institute of Clyde Williams to the new Battelle was a long way from being complete. A new man coming from the academic world would be confronted with a lot of problems that he wouldn't understand. Even if he were extraordinarily intelligent and perceptive, the effect of a failure could be catastrophic."

So the real choice narrowed to just two men. One was Slowter, whom Thomas regarded as "an extremely intelligent administrator." The other was Fawcett, who had been plunged into the thick of Battelle's administrative problems since returning from Battelle-Northwest. The compass needle eventually turned toward Fawcett, probably because he had done a thoroughly competent job of taking on the Hanford laboratory, which had some ticklish problems of its own, and of running an operation involving over 2,500 people.

A nuclear physicist, Fawcett had joined the Columbus Laboratories in 1950, going right into nuclear reactor work. In this Clyde Williams era, he engaged in the approved practice of empire-building with relish. Fawcett took over a division of twenty-seven people and built it up to eighty-three within two years. All that such growth required, he decided, was a job that needed doing and a man to give his all to the job.

Fawcett still believes that every new venture needs "a fanatic" to assure its success, and he is extremely reluctant to start something new if he cannot find a man who is desperately eager to head it. More than once he has played the role himself. He was manager of the Department of Metallurgy and Physics at Columbus when he was selected to establish the new Pacific Northwest Laboratories in 1964. Typically, he arrived at Hanford to announce, "I'm here permanently. I don't even have an office in Columbus any more." And he went to work, convinced that his job was not simply to run the laboratories, but to play a key part in the total development of the Northwest, his newly adopted region.

A strong cast of regionalism continued to color his thinking after he returned to Columbus in 1967, and after he became President of BMI in 1968. Taking off from the long friendship of Thomas and Charles Kimball, president of the Midwest Research Institute in Kansas City, Missouri, Fawcett devised a plan whereby Battelle became, in effect, a major sponsor of regional projects undertaken by Midwest. For this purpose, Fawcett feels that the need was clear, and that the fanatic was ready-made in the person of Kimball.

While Fawcett built on the foundation that Thomas had laid, he did this with his own flair for designing the organization architecture. He has maintained and expanded Battelle Institute, but he has tried to build in some of the incentive principles derived from the approach of private industry. Part of the function that a sponsor performs in contract research, he believes, is that of the goad, giving some needed sense of direction, of goals, and of time pressure. So Fawcett himself supplied a sponsor to ride shotgun on all in-house projects, regardless of how scholarly the subject or how abstruse the aim.

The Fawcett era is only beginning, so it cannot yet be characterized. But Fawcett's personal brand of thinking may offer some clues to what it should mean to Battelle. His own history of Battelle is one that revolves around the limitations that kept the Institute from being better than it is. In the 1930s, 1940s, and up to the mid-1950s, he says, it was capital-limited. Then, as Xerox money quickly overcame that condition, BMI was limited in ideas, partly because of the persistence of the notion that it should merely try to better serve industry and government in the same old fields. Today, with plenty of grand ideas, he says, Battelle is limited in the kind of people it needs to understand the implications of those ideas and to carry them out effectively.

Battelle under Fawcett is using some of its resources to develop the kind of people it wants. The objective is to identify good people, expose them to various parts of the overall operation, and then bring them to the level at which they can do their best work. An investment in people, as seed money, says Fawcett, has capital value.

He looks on Battelle's net worth of $300 million as a resource, but no more than that. If Battelle were to become simply a passive foundation, it could do $18 million worth of work annually on a 6 percent return. But Fawcett believes that the Institute would not then be doing its job, or fulfilling the provisions of Gordon Battelle's will. He would like to see the annual volume of work built up to a point where it would be roughly equal to net worth, with a net income of 4 or 5 percent of this amount for growth. He thinks that plant and physical facilities should have a value of about half of net worth. Since plant is now valued at $100 million, that would indicate a $50 million growth potential in new installations. There are plenty of ideas about where such growth should take place; Fawcett would like to feel confident that they are sound, that they are appropriate to Battelle, that their time has come, and that there are enough fanatics to carry them out.

Fawcett belongs to the new breed of scientist and engineer who look beyond the slide rule to the nature of the problem that is being solved, to the other problems the solution might create, and even to the problems about which no one appears to be yet concerned. He is aware that Battelle will always have to use some of its energies to fight off all those who would like to control it, take it over, or by some means get to the "$300 million that doesn't belong to anybody." So part of his job is simply to assure the Institute's survival; the more important part is making certain that Battelle deserves to survive.

CHAPTER TWELVE

The People of Battelle

Adams, Robert R. [60] * A chemical engineer and metallurgist, he joined Battelle as a co-op student from Antioch College in 1936. He served in a variety of assignments, initially in metallurgical research and subsequently in a broad range of administrative and techno-economic activities. He was named Assistant to the Director in 1941. From 1951 to 1953, he played a key role in the establishment of the Battelle laboratories in Europe, serving as Director of the Frankfurt Laboratories during the first two years. After completing that assignment, he has spent a considerable portion of his subsequent Battelle career as an advisor in overseas activities in Europe and the Middle East.

Albaugh, Fred W. [4] A physical chemist, he joined Battelle in 1965, when Battelle assumed management of the Atomic Energy Commission's Hanford Laboratories, at Richland. Washington. Previously, he was manager of the General Electric Company's Reactor and Fuels Research and Development Operation there. He was named an Associate Director of Battelle's Pacific Northwest Laboratories, and in 1967 was appointed Director. Currently, he is Corporate Director—Sponsored Programs for the Institute, responsible for coordination of energy and environmental research and development activities.

* Designates first reference in text.

Allen, Rolland C. [94] An expert in the field of geology and mining engineering, he was First Vice-President of Oglebay Norton & Company, and, during World War II, held important positions in the War Production Board. He was a Battelle Trustee from 1938 until his death in 1948, serving for a time as President of the Board.

Barnick, Max. [4] He joined Battelle's Frankfurt Laboratories in 1952 as the first staff member, after twenty years of experience in fundamental and industrial research and in research and development for technical associations. He was first named Technical Director and then Director, the title he now holds. He received his education at the University of Berlin, where he later served as a professor. Trained as a physical chemist, he conducted research at the Kaiser-Wilhelm-Institut für Silikatsforschung and then became chief chemist and head of the department of metallurgical physics of Bayerische Motorenwerke. After World War II, he directed the Institut für Blechsverarbeitung until he joined Battelle.

Bird, Byron M. [23] He started the ore-dressing laboratory at Battelle. He joined the staff as a Research Engineer in 1930, and was appointed a Supervisor in 1934. Resigning in 1944, he later served as a consultant to Battelle.

Bixby, William. [40] A physicist, he joined Battelle in 1946 and was associated with early research on the development of xerography in the Graphic Arts Division. He was named a Project Leader in 1956 and left in 1959.

Corbaz, Andre W. [56] A Swiss electrical engineer who joined Battelle-Geneva in 1958. His principal fields of activity have included automation of machinery, measurements, and instrumentation. Coinventor with Poull of electrostatic spinning of yarn.

Crites, Nelson A. [55] He joined Battelle in 1945 as a laboratory technician and was named a research engineer in 1947. He specialized in various experimental stress analysis techniques and has been responsible for the development of a variety of sophisticated devices and instruments, including ultra-thin miniature pressure transducers. He was named an Associate Fellow in 1966 and Research Advisor in 1967.

Cross, Howard C. [25] A chemical engineer, he was a colleague of Horace Gillett at the National Bureau of Standards. He joined Battelle in December of 1929, and his early studies on bearing metals and the high-temperature properties of cast iron led to Battelle's first laboratories for evaluation of the creep properties of metals. During World War II, he organized a cooperative effort on evaluating the creep rupture properties of alloys for high-temperature service, and after the war he undertook coordination of an extensive program including studies of long-range aspects of air and space vehicle propulsion, of propellants, and materials for construction, such as titanium, molybdenum, tungsten, and their alloys. He became Senior Fellow in 1965, and retired in 1969, at which time he became a consultant to Battelle.

Crout, John S. [36] He joined Battelle in 1941 and participated in some of the Institute's earliest technical-economic studies and in subsequent years contributed in diverse ways to Battelle's growth in stature and in service. A mechanical engineer by training, he applied his management skills to the establishment of Battelle laboratories in Europe, the development of the program of the Battelle Development Corporation and of Scientific Advances, Inc., and enhancement of Battelle's position in economics and socio-economics research. As General Manager of the Battelle Development Corporation in 1942, he recognized the potential in Chester Carlson's xerography process and recommended funding its development. He was appointed an Assistant Director of Battelle in 1951, Associate Director in 1953, and Vice President in 1955. He retired in 1964.

Croxton, Frank C. [60] A chemist, he joined Battelle in 1939. From 1943 to 1953, he was in charge of chemical, chemical engineering, and biosciences research, and from 1954 to 1957 was in charge of the European operations. He was appointed an Assistant Director in 1954. Currently, as a member of the Senior Technical Council of Battelle's Columbus Laboratories, he is

113

responsible for assurance of research quality, especially in the areas of chemistry, chemical engineering, economics, and the biosciences.

Dayton, Russell W. [29] A chemical engineer and metallurgist, he joined Battelle as a Research Engineer in 1934. He conducted and supervised bearing and lubrication research, moved into fundamental studies in the machinability of metals, and to research in alternative materials during the early years of World War II. His knowledge of problems of cyclic heat transfer and the physics of the phenomenon was soon applied to the field of reactor materials. He was the first Battelle staff member to meet Chester Carlson and discuss his patent for xerography. He was appointed an Assistant Technical Director in 1953 and an Assistant Director of Technology in 1966. In 1971 he was appointed Coordinator of Battelle Institute Activities. In this capacity he is responsible for Institute-supported research on a worldwide basis.

Derby, Earl Clark. [13] A Columbus industrialist, he was named in Gordon Battelle's will in 1920 as one of four executors of his will and as one of the six original Trustees of Battelle. He served as a Trustee from 1925 until his death in 1943.

Deubner, Russell L. [53] A metallurgical engineer, he joined Battelle as a Research Engineer in 1945. He advanced through various technical and management positions in the Graphic Arts Division and later in the Battelle Development Corporation. He was appointed an Assistant to the Director in 1952 and Manager of the Battelle Development Corporation in 1953. He left in 1958, at which time he became a consultant to Battelle.

Drum, Russell S. [88] He joined Battelle in 1944, and became the first full-time personnel supervisor. He was appointed Personnel Manager in 1953. Under his guidance, the personnel function expanded into the more complex areas of staff relations, counseling, developmental education, health and safety services, pensions and minority recruiting. He died in 1964.

Duncan, Joseph W. [75] An economist, he joined Battelle in 1961 and has conducted various socio-economic studies. He is especially concerned with analysis of socio-economic problems associated with urban development. He served in Washington as Deputy Assistant Secretary for Economic Policy Review for the U.S. Department of Commerce in 1968 and early 1969 while on temporary leave from Battelle. He headed Battelle's Urban Studies Programs prior to his appointment in 1971 as Corporate Co-ordinator of Urban Affairs.

Faust, Charles L. [25] An electrochemical engineer, he joined Battelle in 1934 and established the Electrochemical Engineering Research Division. Its contributions to metal finishing and electro-plating have become world renowned and more than a dozen processes pioneered there have become standard in industry. Faust's research has led to important discoveries involving electro-plating of metals and alloys, metal finishing, electroforming, chemical polishing, electrowinning, electrolysis and electrode processes, process engineering research and development, pickling, and waste disposal. His studies have led to more than 125 patents. He served as Associate Manager in the Department of Chemistry and Chemical Engineering, and as a Senior Technical Advisor prior to his retirement in 1971.

Fawcett, Sherwood L. [5] A nuclear physicist, he joined Battelle in 1950 and participated in research directed toward the development of nuclear reactors for power and naval propulsion. Subsequently, he supervised programs to determine the performance and reliability of reactor fuel and structural components, directed evaluations of reactor concepts, and coordinated engineering and design studies of reactor cooling and moderating systems. Advancing through various managerial assignments, he became the first Director of the Institute's Pacific Northwest Laboratories at Richland, Washington, in 1964. He was elected Executive Vice President of Battelle in 1967 and President in 1968. Since 1969, he also has served as a Battelle Trustee.

Fenton, Gerald B. [14] A cousin of Gordon Battelle and a Business Manager for American Rolling Mill Company serving under Joseph L. Frantz, he has been a Battelle Trustee since 1925. He helped establish the Institute and joined the staff in the dual capacity of Business Manager and Secretary of the Board. As Business Manager, he contributed much to the early planning, organization, and staffing of the Institute. In 1943 he relinquished the active management of the business office in order to devote his efforts to his duties as a Trustee and officer of the Board.

Frantz, Joseph H. [10] Onetime partner in the iron and steel industry of Colonel John Gordon Battelle, Gordon Battelle's father, he was named in Gordon Battelle's will in 1920 as one of the four executors of his will and as one of the six original Trustees of Battelle. He served as a Trustee from 1925 until his death in 1938.

Fuller, Robert W. [78] A theoretical physicist, he joined Battelle as a senior Scientist at the Seattle Research Center in 1967. He resigned in 1968 to become Dean of Faculty at Trinity College and then President of Oberlin College.

Gillett, Horace W. [5] One of the world's foremost metal scientists and a one-time associate of Thomas Edison, he was Director when the Institute began operations in 1929. Before joining Battelle, he was Chief of the Division of Metallurgy of the U.S. Bureau of Standards. He was the inventor of numerous metallurgical processes and author of scores of books and articles on scientific subjects. A scientist rather than an administrator by inclination, he resigned from the directorship of Battelle in 1934, turning the office over to Clyde Williams. From 1934 until 1949 he served as Chief Technical Advisor, in which position he was responsible for the technical guidance of the Institute's research. He died in 1950.

Gonser, Bruce W. [18] A pioneer in the study and development of nonferrous metals, he joined Battelle as a Supervisor in 1934. During his career he gained international recognition for his studies on the properties and development of uses for such metals as titanium, molybdenum, germanium, and zirconium. He was appointed an Assistant Technical Director in 1951 and a Technical Director in 1953. He retired in 1964, at which time he became a consultant to Battelle.

Graves, Edwin E. [42] He joined Battelle in 1941 and conducted research on bearing, lubricants, friction, and surface finishes. He later was engaged in research involving reactor fabrication, and from 1944 to 1947 he served as patent licensing representative for the Battelle Development Corporation. He later conducted and supervised research in the graphic arts, and participated in pioneering work in the development of xerography from a simple laboratory experiment to a successful new process. Since that time he has served in a variety of management positions. He assumed his current post as Administrative Manager of Sponsor and Program Development in 1970.

Gray, John L. [51] An attorney, he joined Battelle in 1949 and was patent counsel until 1952, at which time he was appointed General Counsel. In 1964, he was appointed to his current post as Vice-President and General Manager of the Battelle Development Corporation.

Hamilton, John W. [13] A relative of Gordon Battelle and then President of American University, Washington, D.C., he was named by Gordon Battelle in his will in 1920 as one of the six original Trustees of Battelle. He served as a Trustee from 1925 until his death in 1934.

Harder, Oscar E. [18] Recognized as one of America's most distinguished metallurgists, he joined Battelle as Assistant Director in 1930 and had a major role in the development of the Institute. His research interests encompassed corrosion- and heat-resistant steels, bearing materials, free-machining metals, metal coating, heat treatment and metal fabrication. One of his most noted developments was a tough and corrosion-resistant alloy for watch-springs that was described as the greatest watchmaking advance in over two centuries. His inventions are described in over 100 patents. In 1949 he was appointed a Technical Advisor and entered partial retirement. He became a consultant to Battelle in 1954. He died in 1956.

Harding, Warren G. [13] A friend of Gordon Battelle, he was publisher of *The Marion* (Ohio) *Star* and later the 29th President of the United States (1921–1923). When he was President-elect in 1920, he was named in Gordon Battelle's will as one of the six original Trustees of Battelle. However, he died before the Institute was established in 1925.

Harris, William J., Jr. [82] He joined Battelle as a Metallurgist in 1954 and was appointed Assistant to the Director, Washington, D.C., Offices, in 1955. He left in 1957 to become associated with the National Academy of Sciences-National Research Council. He returned to Battelle as an Associate Manager in 1962 to follow national trends in scientific research and development and undertake related studies. He also managed the Washington Offices. He was appointed Assistant Director of Technology in 1967 and left in 1970 to become Vice President—Research of the American Railroad Association.

Hitt, William D. [73] A psychologist, he joined Battelle in 1957 and has pursued the application of psychological methods to industrial, military, and educational management problems. He was appointed a Research Division Chief in 1962 and has devoted much attention to the study and development of educational management methods and techniques. He was named a Senior Fellow in 1970 and was appointed as Director of Battelle's Center for Improved Education.

Jackson, Lloyd R. [34] An electrical engineer and a physicist, he joined Battelle as an Assistant Supervisor in 1935. Early in his Battelle career, he established a worldwide reputation for his research on the fatigue of metals and structures. He was also a pioneer in the development of selenium rectifiers. He did much to advance Battelle's interdisciplinary approach to large-scale research projects. He also undertook numerous structural analyses and participated in analog- and digital-computer design and development and special instrumentation research, including special optical devices, servo-mechanisms, and optical-inertia system design. He was appointed an Assistant Director—Technology in 1951 and in 1953 was named Coordination Director and was concerned with research administration and planning and forecasting needs for staff, buildings, and equipment. He retired in 1968.

Jaffee, Robert I. [31] A pioneer in the development of titanium, he joined Battelle in 1943 and has served in various technical and administrative capacities. His research interests have emphasized

118

the physical metallurgy of less-common metals, including titanium and refractory metals. He is currently devoting attention to basic and applied research on structural and electronic materials. He has authored or coauthored eight books and several hundred papers and articles, and holds 45 U.S. patents. He was appointed Associate Department Manager in 1968 and Senior Fellow in Materials Science and Technology in 1970.

James, George W. [72] He joined Battelle as a Principal Economist in 1956 and participated in numerous studies relating to research and development management, operations research, area development, and market research. He also investigated factors affecting the business climate of the U.S. and collected data useful in economic forecasting. He was appointed a Research Division Chief in 1961 and as an Associate Research Manager in 1965. He left in 1966 to become a senior vice-president of the Air Transport Association of America.

Jeffries, Zay [28] Described as the "dean of American metallurgy", he served as a professor of metallurgy at Case Institute of Technology and later as a Vice-President of the General Electric Company. He was a pioneer in the development of high-strength aluminum alloys and tungsten metallurgy, and was the recipient of numerous awards. During World War II, he served as vice-chairman of the War Metallurgy Committee of the National Academy of Science-National Research Council and also as a consultant on the atomic bomb project. He was named a Battelle Trustee in 1944, served for many years as Chairman of the Board, and was an Associate Trustee and Honorary Chairman at the time of his death in 1965.

Jewett, Frank B. [102] Chairman of the Board of Bell Telephone Laboratories during World War II, he served as a Battelle Trustee from 1948 until his death in 1949. He also was a former president of the National Academy of Sciences. He was a physicist and electrical engineer by training.

Johnson, Hugo E. [23] He joined Battelle in 1934 and worked as a research assistant at Battelle while studying for his bachelor of science degree in metallurgy at Ohio State University. He was named a Research Engineer in 1940 and later that year left the Institute. After several years in the iron-and-steel industry, he returned to Battelle in 1948, where he assisted in developing research programs in iron and steel. He left in 1953 and is currently president of the American Iron Ore Association.

Keagy, W. Robert, Jr. [60] Joined Battelle in 1946 and, after various technical assignments, was appointed an Assistant to the Director in 1952 and Manager of Battelle's Geneva Laboratories in 1953. He later served as a Staff Department Manager and left Battelle in 1957 to return to Switzerland.

Keinath, Gerald E. [61] A mechanical engineer, he joined Battelle in 1949 and after various technical and management assignments was appointed Assistant Manager of Battelle's Frankfurt Laboratories in 1954. He later served as an Assistant Service Manager and left Battelle in 1963.

Krumlauf, George P. [19] A metallurgist, he joined Battelle in 1937 as a Technical Laboratory Assistant in the foundry and was named a Research Engineer in 1941 working on the mechanical properties of steels. He left Battelle in 1947.

Lorig, Clarence H. [19] A metallurgist, he joined Battelle as a Supervisor in 1930 to conduct research in process metallurgy, foundry practice, blast furnace technology, and related fields. During the next several years he established patterns of metallurgical research that have become traditional with Battelle. He was appointed an Assistant Technical Director in 1947, a Technical Director in 1953, and as a Research Manager in 1962. Prior to his retirement in 1965, he served as Assistant to the President on special assignments nationally and internationally. Upon his retirement, he became a consultant to Battelle.

Martin, William McChesney, Jr. [82] Chairman for nineteen years of the Federal Reserve Board, he was elected an Associate Trustee of Battelle in 1970. He began his career as a stockbroker in the late 1920s and from 1938 to 1941 was president of the New

York Stock Exchange. During World War II, he rose from the rank of private to colonel, and after the war served as Chairman of the Board of the Export-Import Bank, Assistant Secretary of the Treasury, and U.S. Executive Director for the International Bank for Reconstruction and Development.

Merrill, Roger L. [4] An electrical engineer, he joined Battelle and participated in research dealing with electronics, control systems, and computers. His name appears on eighteen U.S. and foreign patents. Before assuming his present position in 1970 as Director of Battelle's Columbus Laboratories, he served as Associate Director, as Assistant Director for Technical Development, and as Manager of the Engineering Physics research department.

Minton, David C., Jr. [4] A mining and metallurgical engineer who taught at the University of Arizona and the University of the Philippines, he joined Battelle in 1941 with the Battelle Development Corporation. During World War II, he was on leave from Battelle and served from 1942 to 1945 in Washington, where he administered portions of the nation's metallurgical research with the War Metallurgy Committee. He returned to the Institute as Assistant to the Director, and, over the years, held varied administrative responsibilities. In the early 1950s, he participated in the establishment of the Battelle laboratories in Geneva and Frankfurt. He was appointed Associate Director in 1953, Vice President in 1955, and Director of Battelle's Columbus Laboratories in 1964, serving in that capacity until 1970. During his Directorship he had an active role in the development of coastal research facilities to enhance Battelle's ocean research capabilities. Currently, he is Vice President-Sponsor Relations, representing Battelle on a worldwide basis.

Murdock, John W. [33] A physicist, he joined Battelle in 1951 and performed microwave and radar research. Since 1953, he has been concerned with research related to storage and retrieval of scientific information and in management of information analysis centers. He served in various technical and management assignments at Battelle-Columbus before being named Manager of the Information Systems Section in 1970.

121

Nestor, Myron R. (Mike) [92] A metallurgical engineer, he joined Battelle in 1935 and participated in extensive studies on new exhaust valve materials and developed techniques for determining the suitability of these materials. He later served as a research coordinator and in 1945 began devoting full time to project development assignments. In 1951, he was appointed as an Assistant to the Director, and, from 1952, he served as Manager of project development activities for many years. He retired in early 1972.

Nielsen, Kaj L. [75] He joined Battelle in 1963, first as a consultant and later that year as a Systems Analysis Group Director. His group conducted studies in problems related to weapon systems, the automatic checkout of space and other equipment, ocean engineering, and transportation. He was appointed as a Senior Advisor in 1965, and retired in 1971 after a period of splitting his time between Battelle and the Central Ohio Transit Authority.

Oughton, Charles D. [40] A physicist, he joined Battelle in 1945 as a Research Engineer in the Graphic Arts Division during the development of xerography. He coauthored, along with Roland Schaffert, the first technical paper describing the process. He was named as an Assistant Supervisor in 1946 and left in 1950.

Paul, Ronald S. [4] A physicist, he joined Battelle in 1965 when the Institute assumed management of the Hanford Laboratories at Richland, Washington. Previously he had served since 1951 with the General Electric Company's Hanford Atomic Products Operation at Richland, where he performed and managed research in nuclear physics and atmospheric sciences. He was appointed Associate Director of Battelle's Northwest Laboratories in 1966, Deputy Laboratory Director in 1967, and Director of the Battelle Seattle Research Center and Coordinator of Battelle Institute Activities in 1968. In 1971, he was named to his present position as Director of Battelle-Northwest.

Pierce, John R. [82] He was elected an Associate Trustee of Battelle in 1961 and has served as a Trustee since 1963. Currently an engineering professor at the California Institute of Technology, he retired in 1971 as Executive Director, Research Communication

Sciences Division of the Bell Telephone Laboratories. He is noted for his role in the Echo I satellite project and holds fifty-five patents relating to electron tubes and microwave research. In 1963, he was awarded the National Medal of Science by President Johnson.

Poull, Maurice R. [56] A French mathematician and engineer who joined Battelle-Geneva in 1964, where he presently heads the Electromechanical Devices and Textile Machinery Division. From 1951 until joining Battelle, gained wide experience in the organization and management of textile mills and textile research and development. Coinventor of electrospin, a method of electrostatic spinning of yarn.

Pray, Henry A. H. (Gus) [98] A physical chemist, he joined Battelle in 1934 and gained recognition for his studies on the fundamentals of corrosion and electrochemical technologies, including the development of electroplating and electropolishing techniques. He is the coinventor of a chemical polishing process patented in 1948 and still in use. Also bearing his name are patents on coatings for metals and metal pipe, and on processes for preparing alumina and for free-machining stainless steels containing bismuth. He was appointed an Assistant Technical Director in 1953. He retired in 1962, at which time he became a consultant to Battelle.

Raab, Charles F. [20] He joined Battelle as Chief of Shops in 1929 and left in 1942. He was praised as a "technician who could make almost anything that was needed."

Richards, George [40] He joined Battelle as a Laboratory Assistant in 1943 and was named a Research Engineer in 1944. He became associated with the Graphic Arts Division in 1945 and participated in early work on the development of xerography. He left later that year.

Richardson, Albert C. [24] A mining and metallurgical engineer, he joined Battelle as an Assistant Supervisor in 1933. He served in various technical positions before being named a Supervisor in 1942 and a Technical Director in 1953. He played a prominent role in building Battelle's reputation in the fields of minerals beneficiation and extractive metallurgy. He is known particularly for his contributions to increasing the availability of three vital materials—uranium, iron, and coal. After the Manhattan Project first emphasized the urgent need for uranium, he guided much of Battelle's early research to find the best method for processing this vital material. These studies included the recovery of uranium from phosphate rock and shale, North Dakota lignites, and carnotite ores. He retired in 1963, at which time he became a consultant to Battelle.

Roberts, Dimon A. [21] A mechanical engineer and metallurgist, he joined Battelle as a Research Engineer in 1936 and worked with Oscar Harder in the development of a tough and durable new alloy for watchsprings—described as the greatest advance in watchmaking in over two centuries. He later served as an Assistant Division Consultant and as a Senior Metallurgist. He retired in 1966.

Runkle, Harry M. [13] A Columbus attorney and business associate of Gordon Battelle, he was named in Gordon Battelle's will in 1920 as one of four executors of his will and as one of the six original Trustees of Battelle. He served as a Trustee from 1925 until his death in 1962.

Russell, Howard W. [18] One of the original members of the staff, he was brought to Battelle in 1929 by Horace Gillett because of his intuitive belief that physics would play a role in the development of metallurgy. During World War II, he headed Battelle's major effort in the Manhattan District of the U. S. Army Corps of Engineers, as the atomic bomb program was then known. A veteran Atomic Energy Commission research administrator recalls that Russell and his staff "wrote the book on uranium metallurgy, including rolling, extrusion, and wire-drawing." His technical and scientific writings cover such diverse subjects as reactor fuel elements, physical properties of materials, corrosion technology, electrochemistry, pyrometry, and x-ray and electron diffraction. United States and foreign patents credited to him cover work with internal combustion engines, metal alloys, heat transfer devices, and temperature recording instruments. He was appointed an Assistant Technical Director in 1947 and a Technical Director in 1953. He died in 1965.

Schaffert, Roland M. [38] A printer and later a research physicist in the printing equipment industry, he joined Battelle in 1941 as a Research Engineer to work on printing projects. He was among the Battelle staff members who attended the first meeting at the Institute with Chester Carlson, inventor of xerography. In a memorandum of April 5, 1944, on xerography, he concluded: "This process looks like a good research gamble." He established the Graphic Arts Division in the fall of 1944, headed the developmental research on xerography, and was one of those who first described the process publicly on October 22, 1948, before the annual meeting of the Optical Society of America in Detroit. He was appointed a Technical Advisor in 1950 and an Assistant Department Consultant in 1955. He left Battelle in 1956.

Schnee, Verne H. [28] He joined Battelle as a Research Engineer in 1935 and was appointed a Supervisor in 1941. During World War II, he served with other Battelle staff members on the War Metallurgy Committee. He later was named an Assistant to the Director, responsible for project development. He left in 1949, becoming a consultant to Battelle in 1952. He died in 1957.

Schwarz, Albert [62] He joined Battelle's Laboratories as an Assistant to the Director in 1952, serving in various management positions before being appointed Supervisor of Public Relations for the laboratories.

Seckendorff, Ernst W. [89] He joined Battelle as Assistant to the Director in 1934 and developed a cost accounting system to help determine the allocation of "a multitude of small charges to the appropriate accounts." He also established a system for both financial and operating control of the various divisions and departments. He resigned in 1937.

Sherman, Ralph A. [24] He was brought to Battelle in 1930 by Horace Gillett from the Bureau of Mines where he had worked on fuels and combustion. The fundamental research he conducted on the combustion of pulverized coal and on radiation from flames of pulverized coal and of natural gas, during his first years at the Institute, stand as classics in combustion literature and made him an internationally known figure in combustion research. He was in direct charge of a major long-term research program on coal for more than a decade. More than 100 technical papers carry his name as author or coauthor. He was appointed a Technical Director in 1947 and retired in 1961, at which time he became a consultant to Battelle.

Sims, Clarence E. [19] He joined Battelle in 1936 as Supervising Metallurgist in process and physical metallurgy. He was closely associated with many investigations on steelmaking processes and also supervised studies on factors influencing the oxygen, nitrogen, sulfur, and inclusion contents of steels produced in a variety of melting furnaces. He is the author or coauthor of more than eighty technical papers. He was appointed as a Technical Director in 1947 and held that position until his retirement in 1958, at which time he became a consultant to Battelle.

Slowter, Edward E. [89] Battelle's Vice President, Director of General Administration, Secretary, and Treasurer, he had his first association with the Institute while a graduate student at The Ohio State University and the recipient of a Battelle fellowship. A chemical engineer, he joined Battelle in 1934 as a Research Associate and was named a Research Engineer in 1936. His chemical research studies led him successively into work with patents and patent applications, research contracts and contract administration, and finally financial and policy matters. He entered the service in 1942. Returning in 1945, he became responsible for contracts and eventually all business office operations and nontechnical areas. He was appointed Assistant to the Director in 1951, Business Manager in 1953, Associate Director in 1955, and Vice President in 1962.

Smith, Frank P. (Pop) [20] Smith was one of the early Battelle staff members; he joined Battelle in 1930 as a technician. Highly regarded for his skill as a machinist, he served in a variety of laboratory assignments in ore dressing, metallurgy, and the foundry. He retired in 1952 and died in 1962.

Stith, Robert O. [43] He joined Battelle in 1933 and was involved in pioneering studies on plating from the vapor phase before assum-

126

ing administrative responsibilities in 1938. These included the coordination of public relations activities. He undertook the assignment of finding a more suitable name than "electrophotography" for Chester Carlson's dry-copying process. The name finally selected was "xerography." He was appointed an Assistant to the Director in 1952 and Public Relations Manager in 1953.

Sullivan, John D. [18] An analytical and physical chemist, he joined Battelle as a Supervisor in 1931 and helped establish the Institute as a center for ceramics research. He conducted studies on the surface chemistry of clays, the development of metallurgical refractories, did pioneering work on the production of lightweight aggregates from clay and shales, and studied methods for enameling copper. He was placed in charge of the Battelle Development Corporation shortly after its formation in 1935, while still heading the Ceramics and Process Metallurgy Divisions. He also inaugurated Institute studies for industry on the economics of metal and mineral processing and maintained extensive files on such aspects as costs and pricing, industry competitive structure, and supply and demand. Additionally, he was interested in industrial gases and fuels. During World War II, he served with other Battelle staff members on the War Metallurgy Committee and was chairman of its process research division. In 1947, he was appointed an Assistant Director, and in 1953 he was named a Technical Director. He retired in 1965, at which time he became a consultant to Battelle.

Thiemann, Hugo [4] He joined Battelle's Geneva Laboratories in 1953 to organize the Division of Applied Physics and Electrical Engineering. He was appointed Director in 1954. A graduate of the Federal Institute of Technology of Zurich, where he was Assistant to the Director of the Institute of Applied Physics, he worked in various fields of applied physics, optics, and television, and headed research on the development of a large-screen television projection system.

Thomas, Bertram D. [5] A chemist, he joined Battelle as a Supervisor in 1934 and established the Institute's Chemical Research

Division in 1939. He also was instrumental in organizing the Institute's first patent staff. He was appointed an Assistant Director in 1942. Subsequently, he was named Secretary of the Battelle Memorial Institute Corporation and Vice-President in 1955. He was named Director in 1956, President-Director in 1958, and President in 1962. A scientist-philosopher, he led the Institute into a multitude of new fields and established close ties with the academic community. He was instrumental in the establishment of the Battelle research centers in Frankfurt, Geneva, and Richland, Washington. He also established Battelle Institute, a component designed to fund and explore fields not yet ripe for contract research, and the Battelle Seattle Research Center, a site for theoretical studies and scientific seminars. He was also instrumental in Battelle's entrance into the field of social economics research. He retired as President in 1968, but still serves as a Trustee, a position to which he was elected in 1966.

Walkup, Lewis E. [40] An electrical engineer, he joined Battelle as a Research Engineer in the Graphic Arts Division in 1946. One of Batelle's most innovative scientists, he played key roles as experimenter, technical supervisor, and overseer of creative analysis in the development of xerography. The majority of his more than 100 patents were granted for inventions related to that process. Other studies in which he participated were directed toward use of electrostatic energy for industrial processes; unusual concepts for micro-image projectors and readers, and the development of a prepress color-proofing process. In 1953 he was named a Research Division Chief. He wrote and lectured extensively on the theme that technical creativity can and should be cultivated. He retired in 1970.

Welcker, William A., Jr. [15] A mechanical engineer, he joined Battelle as one of the original staff members in 1929 and was made responsible for all purchasing, building maintenance, and, in time, new construction. As the Institute grew, he took charge of the physical testing laboratory, the heat-treating laboratory, the metallographic laboratory, photographic laboratory, first-aid facilities, general utility functions, and visitor reception and guidance. In 1937 he was put in charge of all physical facilities. He headed building construction and plant management during a period of great physical growth and was concerned in one way or another with almost every building and addition since Battelle's original expansion in the 1930s. He played a key role in the construction of the Institute's nuclear science facilities at the West Jefferson (Ohio) site and participated in the planning studies concerning the physical facilities for the laboratories in Frankfurt and Geneva. He was appointed a Supervisor in 1944, an Assistant to the Director in 1952, Property Manager in 1953, a Senior Technical Advisor in 1962, and a Senior Technical Representative in 1965. He retired in 1970.

Wheeler, John A. [8] A noted physicist and a leading figure in the development of the atomic and hydrogen bombs, he is Joseph Henry Professor of Physics at Princeton University. In the past two decades he has made major contributions in such fields as nuclear fission, cosmic ray physics, transformations of atomic nuclei and elementary particles, and general relativity. Recipient of many awards for his scientific achievements, he received the National Medal of Science from President Nixon in 1970. He has served as a Battelle Trustee since 1959 and currently is First Vice Chairman of the Board.

Williams, Clyde E. [5] A chemical engineer, he joined Battelle as Assistant Director in 1929 and was appointed Director in 1934, President and Director in 1953, and President in 1956. He pioneered in the concept of contract research for industrial development, initiated and assisted in the organization and management of many industrial research agencies, and headed Battelle during the years of expansion in Europe. During World War II, he served as Chairman of the War Metallurgy Committee, which advised the War Production Board on problems of production and conservation of metals and ores of strategic importance to the conduct of the war. He was also Chairman of the War Metallurgy Division of the Office of Scientific Research and Development. After World War II, he served on numerous government advisory committees dealing with research advice and management. He retired from Battelle in 1957.

Wise, Edward N. [40] A chemist, he joined Battelle as a Research Engineer in 1945 in the Graphic Arts Division, where he participated in early work on the development of xerography. At the time, he was one of the Institute's top technical authorities on photography. He left in 1947.

About the Authors

George A. W. Boehm was born in New York City and spent his early years in Asheville, N. C. He attended Men's College at Columbia University in New York. He did graduate work in mathematics at Columbia, from which he received both his B.S. and M.S. degrees.

He has spent the largest part of his working career as a magazine writer. In 1954 he became Managing Editor of *Control Engineering,* published by McGraw-Hill. The following year he was appointed to the Board of Editors of *Scientific American.* From 1956 through 1966, Mr. Boehm was Science-Technology Editor of *Fortune,* published by Time Inc.

Since 1966 he has been a free-lance writer, contributing principally to *Think, Reader's Digest,* the *New York Times Sunday Magazine,* and preparing special reports of the National Academy of Sciences.

He is the author of *The New World of Math,* published by Dial Press in 1959. Mr. Boehm is a member of the American Mathematical Society, the New York Academy of Sciences, and the National Association of Science Writers.

A native of Cleveland, Ohio, **Alex Groner** has spent most of his career in journalism—as a reporter, correspondent, writer, and editor. On graduating from Case Western Reserve University, he went to work for the Cleveland *Press,* serving variously as a reporter, assistant financial editor, rewrite man, and editorial writer, from 1937 to 1951. His newspaper work was punctuated by Army service from 1942 to 1945.

From 1948 to 1951 Mr. Groner was a part-time correspondent for *Time, Life,* and *Fortune.* He joined the *Time* writing staff as a contributing editor in 1951. In 1954 he became the Corporate Historian of Time Inc., and compiled a voluminous set of historical records for the company. He wrote a number of annual reports to the shareholders of Time Inc., and he initiated a training program for junior editorial personnel, in connection with the company's employee newspaper. In 1962 he became Manager of Internal Communications for Time Inc.

In 1965 he was on a special assignment for the Research and Development Department of Time Inc., traveling extensively around the world to study education and educational needs. At the end of that assignment, he was named Assistant to the Director of Corporate Development. He served on a number of task forces that worked on early planning for General Learning Corporation, the educational affiliate formed by Time Inc. and General Electric Company.

Mr. Groner's education includes a degree in literature from Case Western Reserve University and subsequently study in engineering at the University of Illinois. He has a law degree from Cleveland Marshall Law School and is a member of the bar of the State of Ohio.